Visual (

Coasta
Santa

MW00619031

George L. Pikkarainen

Pikkdata

Dedication

This book is dedicated to my daughters
Gwen and Kate

Special thanks go to Dorene Smith, a superb naturalist, who helped me with many identification problems and reviewed my early work. Errors in this book are mine, not Dorene's. I would also like to thank Wilma Fonte, Bob Soost and others for putting up with me on their native plant society walks, their help in field identification and in providing resource materials.

Thanks to my good buddy Marlys Green for the hours she spent helping me organize my data files and to about 4000 Biology students who provided the incentive to make Botany more interesting, by providing visual cues in place of vocabulary.

Appreciation to my parents who instilled the "Sisu" needed to complete this project. and finally to my wife Molly who put up with my hermit like behavior during the 3 plus years it took to do the book.

I solicit your comments or corrections and
provide purchasing information at
Pikkdata@Yahoo.com

First printing March 2002

ISBN 0-9718414-0-3

Table of contents

Introduction

This is a book for beginners and students who lack experience with taxonomic language keys. Major plant groups like ferns and conifers have simple distinctive visible traits. With over 100 local families, dicots are more difficult to key. Pictures and brief statements are provided for 19 of the most common dicot families. The habitat icon key and pictures showing species traits should simplify the identification of most plants.

Most books of bay area plants were written in the 1960's or 1970's. Since then, computer database and DNA analysis has resulted in numerous scientific name changes. I have attempted to provide previous scientific names for the plants in this book. Re-evaluation of names is an ongoing process, and a few names may be changed even as this book is being published.

My goal was to provide a field guide that fits in a pocket. To conserve space and size, information about each species has been compressed onto a data card. The data cards provide page number reference to books used in compilation of this book which have more wordy descriptions.

E) Elke — "Wild Flowers of Marin"
A @C Pillpott. The Tamalpais Press. 1979
(F) Ferris. — "Flowers of Point Reyes National Seashore".
University of California Press 1970
(G) Gladys Smith — "Flowers and Ferns of Muir Woods".
Muir Woods Natural History Association. 1963.
(M) Munz — "Shore Wildflowers of California, Oregon and Washington". University of California Press 1964
(P) Peterson — "Field Guide to Pacific States Wildflowers".
Houghton Mifflin Company, Boston. 1976.
(S) Sharsmith — "Spring Wildflowers of the San Francisco Bay Region". University of California Press 1965
(W) Metcalf, W— "Native Trees of the San Francisco Bay Region". University of California Press 1966
(Z) Grillos — "Ferns and Fern Allies".
University of California Press 1966

Other references used in compiling the book
Jepson Manual, James C Hickman (Editor)
University of California Press, 1993
Plants of the San Francisco Bay Region,
Kozolff @ Beidleman Sagon Press, 1994
Marin Flora, Howell, University of California Press, 1970
Jepson Manual Changes to " Marin Flora" 1994 (Pamplet)
Field checklists and name updates. Marin Chapter of the California Native Plant Society, and numerous other unidentifed sources.

Some Good Flower locations

Fort Bragg

Mendocino
VanDamme St. Pk.

Mendocino Co.

Point Arena

Willits

Sea Ranch

Russian
River
Valley

Salt Point St. Pk.

Fort Ross St. Pk

Sonoma Co.

Napa
Valley

Bodega Bay
and Dunes

Santa
Rosa

Pt.Reyes Nat. Seashore

Marin Co.

San Rafael

Mt. Tamalpais St. Pk.
Muir Woods Nat Mon

San Francisco

Oakland

San Mateo Co.

Butano St. Pk

Ano Nueve Pt

San Jose

Big Basin St.Pk

Santa Clara Co.

Santa Cruz Co.

Santa Cruz

Monterey

Pt Lobos Nat Shore

Monterey
Co.

Big Sur St Pk.

BC-Can

WA

NW

OR

ID

Cst
Mts

SN
Mts

NV

CA

SW

SW

MEX

Baja

Western States range areas

A 3

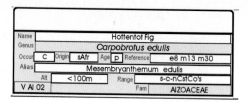

Name	Hottentot Fig					
Genus	*Carpobrotus edulis*					
Occur	C	Origin	sAfr	Age	p	Reference	e8 m13 m30
Alias	Mesembryanthemum edulis					
	Alt	<100m		Range		s-c-nCstCo's
V AI 02					Fam	AIZOACEAE

Data Card Reference

ICONS - Describe habitat @ habit. The icons may not match the environment where you found a specimen. You may have a waif in a less then ideal location or sub species or species not in the book. .

NAME - Common names vary. I have tried to include multiple common names when more then one name is used locally.

GENUS -Genus and species. Technical papers written use this latinized name in their title and work. Researchers may claim and name what they think is a new species. Later studies may show that the "new species" belongs to another group or a previously named plant. The "new species" name must revert to the to the original name. The **ALIAS** Line contains outdated Latin names

OCCUR **C** (Common) **LC**(Locally Common) **O**(occasional) **U**(Uncommon) **R**(Rare) **End**(Endangered **Exc** (Escape) **Cult** (Cultivated **Waif** (Escape)

ORIGIN **Native** (NativeCa) **s**-South **c**- Central **n**- North **e**- East **w**-West

Afr (Africa))	**China**	**MidE** (MiddleEast)
Amer (America))	**Eur** (Europe)	**NZ** (New Zealand)
Asia (Asia)	**Hemis** (Hemisphere)	**PacIs** (Pacific Isl
Aus (Australia)	**Med** (Mediteranian)	**Trop** (Tropics)
Can (Canada)	**Mex** (Mexico)	**US** (United States)

Ala (Alaska)	**CstCo's** Coast Counties	**SN** (Sierra Navada Mtns)
Baja (Mexico)	**CstCo's** Coast Counties	**SW** (Southwestern States)
BC (British Columbia)	**GV** (Ca. Great Valley)	**Wa** (Washington)
Ca/Cal (California)	**NW** (N. Western States)	**WStates** (Rocky Mtns)
Co's (Counties)	**Ore**(Oregon)	(to WCoast)

AGE **a**(Annual) **b**(Bi-annual **p**(Perennual) **S**(Shrub) **T**(Tree)

REFERENCE Local books w/ discriptive information (Introduction Page)

ALTITUDE

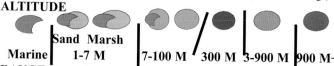

Marine	**Sand**	**Marsh**				
	1-7 M		7-100 M	300 M	3-900 M	900 M+

RANGE Geographic range within the book and West Coast region

CARD Identification Number

FAMILY Scientific Latin Name (Jepson Manual)

ICONS

Wet, Warm, Winter

Flower Season   Jan Feb Mar Apr May Jun Jul Aug Sep Oct Nov Dec

Dry, Cold, Winter

Bog   **Loam**   **Clay**   **Sand**

Full Sun

Part Shade

Serpentine   **Hardpan**   **Rock, Gravel**   **Disturbed**

Shade

Banks Cliffs   **Hillsides**   **Ridges Slopes**

Spring Grass

Grass Grassland

Dry grass

Damp, Wet Soil

Arid landscapes deserts

Flats   **Hollows**   **Canyon, Ravine**

Pine, Conifer   Bay Laural Oak,

Soft brush   Coastal scrub

Mixed Woods   **Mixed broad Leaf**   Chaparal

Meadows Open woods

Open brush, Edge of Brush

Dry washes Stream Beds   Stream side Grassland   **Riperian woods**   Pond and Lake Edge   Springs Seeps

---

Marine climate   Foredunes   Mid dunes   Estuary Marshes   Coastal Bluff

Beach   Stable Dune

Agriculture Domestic   Roadside   Timber Cuts   After fires   **X** Special conditions

A 5

Plant Communities

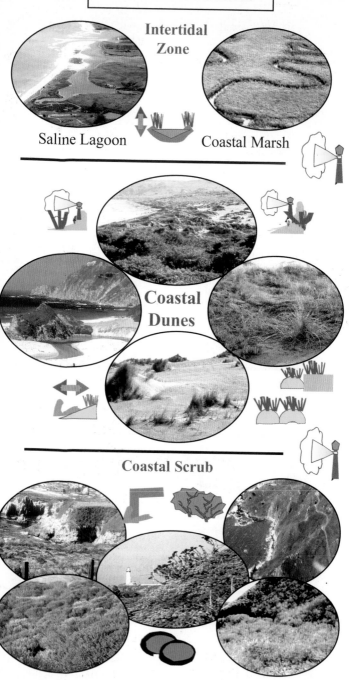

Intertidal Zone

Saline Lagoon

Coastal Marsh

Coastal Dunes

Coastal Scrub

A 6

Sand-Clay   Serpentine

Chapparal

Jan Feb Mar Apr May Jun Jul Aug Sep Oct Nov Dec

February   Grassland   July
April

Oak Woodland

Buckeye
and Bay
laurel

Madrone and
Tanbark Oak

Alder and Bay Laurel   Conifers

A 7

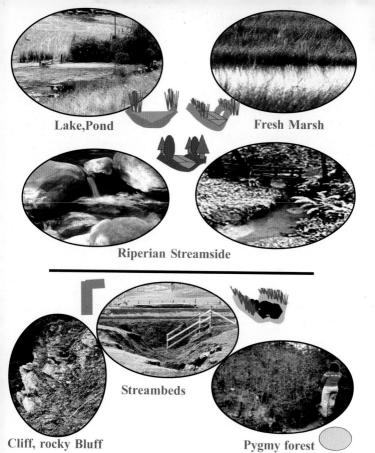

Lake, Pond

Fresh Marsh

Riperian Streamside

Streambeds

Cliff, rocky Bluff

Pygmy forest

Disturbed

A 8

Visual Key to Major Plant Groups

SECTION 1 SPORE PLANTS (Ferns and Horsetails)

Fern spores form in sori (bag like structures) on the under side of fronds. Mature sori burst in a unique way to release the spores.

Horsetails Spores form in crevices of the terminal spore case. When mature the crevices widen to expose and release the spores.

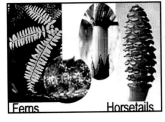

Ferns   Horsetails

SECTION 2 Class GYMNOSPERMAE (Gymnosperms)

Seeds (embryo with food + shell) generally form on the plates of a cone. Mature cones open to permit the seeds to drop out. Ginko trees lack cones.

Pines Junipers Cypresses etc

Gymnosperms are all trees or woody shrubs. Leaves are in the form of slender or blunt scaly needles. One imported non-native species (Ginko) has fan shaped leaves.

SECTIONS 3,4,5, Class ANGIOSPERMAE (Angiosperms)

Flowering plants with seeds enclosed in a protective covering (ovary). The ovary, and sometimes other surrounding tissues develop into a fruit. . When mature the fruit opens or rots to release the seeds.

A 9

SECTION 3 Subclass MONOCOTYLEDONAE

(Monocots in many books

Seeds with 1 seed leaf + one cotyledon (food storage area)

In monocots, vascular bundles form from a central bud

(meristem). In cross section, the stem (pedicel) shows scattered vascular bundles along with non-specialized filler tissues. An outer line of bundles can split free from the pedicel to form a parallel vein leaf. The

vast majority of monocots are annuals or biannual which regenerate from bulbs, corms, or rhizomes.

Examples of the 5 most common local families are shown below.

Iridaceae

Liliaceae

Cyperaceae

Juncaceae

Poaceae

SECTIONS 4 and 5 SUBCLASS DICOTYLEDAE (Dicots)

Seeds with 2 seed leaves + 2 cotyledons (Food storage areas)

Flower parts (sepals, petals, and stamens) are usually in sets of 4's or 5's, Most have distinct net vein pinnate or palmate leaves. In the stem a group of vascular bundles form a ring with pithy filler at the stem core. A cambian (new tissue generating layer) separates the phloem (outer part of the bundle) from the xylem (inner part of the bundle). In woody dicots, the cambian layer generates a new ring of vascular tissue each year. The outer part of the older bundle hardens to form a ring of bark or cork and the inner part of the old bundle hardens to become a ring of wood

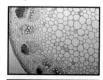

This book breaks the dicots into 3 sections
Section 4   Woody dicots (Trees, Vines, Shrubs)
Section 5a Common non-wood dicot Families
Section 5b Non-wood Dicot families with few local species

SECTION 4 WOODY DICOT PLANTS

Trees generally have one major trunk emerging from the ground.   Most are over 2.5 meters (about 9 Feet) tall.

Shrubs and Scrub generally has numerous small woody stems branching from or near ground level.

Woody vine a flexible net of slender woody branches

3 Woody dicot families with numerous local species are shown

Vase with flared lip, Fused petals Most with leathery leaves
Reddish bark Often shedding   Ericaceae

Trees   Acorns (Most)
Leathery leaves (Most)
Fagaceae

Stiff bramble of branches
Unique flower   Rhamnaceae

SECTION 5 NON WOODY DICOTS

Annuals and bi-annual herbal plants with a soft or fiber like stem tissues, and perennials with woody roots which regrow the soft above ground stems and leaves each year. Some common non-woody dicot families have a few genera or species of woody plants.

Mostly non woody dicot families in this book having a number of common woody species include

Asteraceae, Fabaceae, Rosaceae and Scropulariaceae

There are well over 100 families of dicot plants in this area. Over 75% ot the more common or interesting dicot species are in one of 19 common families. The following pages offer clues to to simplify your search within these 19 famillies. These families are marked with distinguishing color bars. In the body of the book, these families are marked with the same identifying color bar

Smaller dicot families are not marked with color codes and make up the final part of the book.

5 petals 5 stamens alternate to petals   Often with licorice or other odor
Umbel (usually 2 levels)   Leaves often lacy
Apiaceae

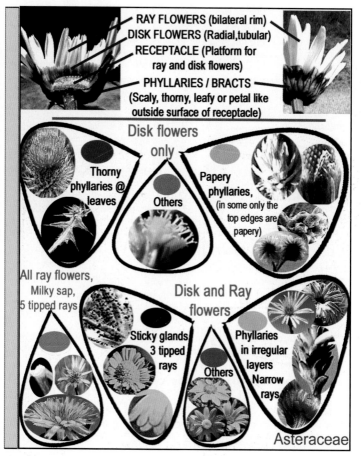

RAY FLOWERS (bilateral rim)
DISK FLOWERS (Radial,tubular)
RECEPTACLE (Platform for
ray and disk flowers)
PHYLLARIES / BRACTS
(Scaly, thorny, leafy or petal like
outside surface of receptacle)

Disk flowers
only

Thorny
phyllaries @
leaves

Others

Papery
phyllaries,
(in some only the
top edges are
papery)

All ray flowers,
Milky sap,
5 tipped rays

Sticky glands
3 tipped
rays

Disk and Ray
flowers

Others

Phyllaries
in irregular
layers
Narrow
rays

Asteraceae

5 Base fused petals form a tube, stamens form a tube throat ring
Most leaves w/o petiole   Most with coiled flower head   **Boraginaceae**

Unusual flower head

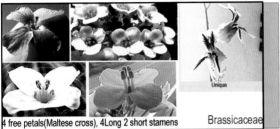

4 free petals(Maltese cross), 4Long 2 short stamens   Brassicaceae

Unique

5 petals Many with deep bi-lobed petals
Most leaves opposite and clasping stem   Caryphyllaceae

Unique flowers

Twisted bud, Fused petals
Vine like,   Arrowhead Leaf
Convolvulaceae

5 free petals Unique fruit
Deep cut leaves
Geraniaceae

Unique bilateral "PEA" flower (Petals project from banner)
Unique legume fruit   Fabaceae

5 fused lobed petals   Sepals alternate to petals
Spiral of flowers   Hydrophyllaceae

Bilateral (2 petal upper lip @ 3 lower or 3lobed lower lip) Flower
5 petals fused at base   Many with mint fragrance   Laminaceae

5 fused petals drop off together   Most with many stamens
Stamens a fused tube Malvaceae   4(6) free Petals   Papavaceae

4 free petals 4 free stamens alternate to petals
Stigma tip a ball or forming a cross, Inferior ovary   Onagraceae

5 Fused funnel petals 5 stamens alternate to petals
Many w/ linear leaf rosettes at the base of flowers   Polemoniaceae

A 14

Floral rosettes at nodes or umbel of flowers at stem tips
Most with swollen stem nodes   Polygonaceae

Opposite sessile leaves
Petals 5, fused base   Portulaceae

5(6,10)Petals Many stamens Many pistils   Radial and bilateral flowers
Many have spherical fruit with numerous prickle tips   Ranuculaceae

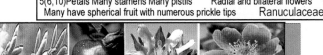

Many w/ inferior ovary Many domestic fruit/berries   Some thorny stems
5-10Petals, Many stamens, Many pistils   Roseaceae

5 fused petals Tubular 2 lipped (2 fused lobes up and 3 lobed down)
Leaves narrow to linear   Scrophulariaceae

A 15

Spore bearing plants

Horsetails, and Ferns

Other less common groups not shown in this book
Quillworts, Club Mosses, Spike mosses and Adders Tongue
Families

Name	Common Horsetail					
Genus	*Equisetum arvense*					
Occur	C	Origin	Native	Age	p	Reference	z17
Alias						
Alt				Range	s-c-nCstCo's SN	
F aEQ 01				Family	````EQUISETACEAE	

Name	Giant Horsetail					
Genus	*Equisetum telmateia var. braunii*					
Occur	O	Origin	Native	Age	p	Reference	g29 m10 m27 z21
Alias						
Alt				Range	c-nCstCo's - BC	
F aEQ 02				Family	````EQUISETACEAE	

Name	Giant Chain Fern					
Genus	*Woodwardia fimbriata*					
Occur	C-Cult	Origin	Native	Age	p	Reference	g29 z48
Alias	Single pinnate, Black indusia, Smooth green stem					
Alt				Range	s-c-nCstCo's, GV, SN, wUS	
F BL 01				Family	```BLECHNACEAE	

Name	Western Bracken Fern					
Genus	*Pteridium aquilinum var. pubescens*					
Occur	C-Cult	Origin	Native	Age	p	Reference	g27 m10 z74
Alias	Double pinnate, No indusia, Green,hairly tan stem					
Alt				Range	s-c-nCstCo's US World	
F DE 01				Family	```DENNSTAEDTIACEAE	

Single Pinnate

No Indusia

Black smooth Stipe

Double Pinnate

Horseshoe Indusia

Tan Smooth

Sword like hilt

Sori hidden (folded pinna edge)

Green w/tan hair

60 cm

15 cm

2 cm

3 cm

80 cm

40 cm

6 cm

2 cm

4 cm

1 M

30 cm

2 M

1 cm

60 cm

30cm

2 cm

F 3

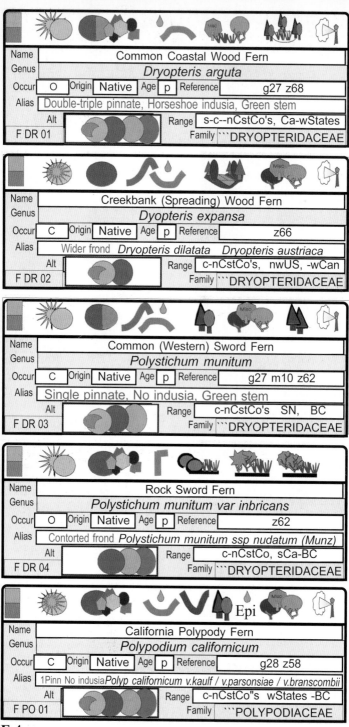

Name	Common Coastal Wood Fern
Genus	*Dryopteris arguta*
Occur	O	Origin	Native	Age	p	Reference	g27 z68
Alias	Double-triple pinnate, Horseshoe indusia, Green stem
Alt		Range	s-c--nCstCo's, Ca-wStates
F DR 01		Family	```DRYOPTERIDACEAE

Name	Creekbank (Spreading) Wood Fern
Genus	*Dyopteris expansa*
Occur	C	Origin	Native	Age	p	Reference	z66
Alias	Wider frond *Dryopteris dilatata* *Dryopteris austriaca*
Alt		Range	c-nCstCo's, nwUS, -wCan
F DR 02		Family	```DRYOPTERIDACEAE

Name	Common (Western) Sword Fern
Genus	*Polystichum munitum*
Occur	C	Origin	Native	Age	p	Reference	g27 m10 z62
Alias	Single pinnate, No indusia, Green stem
Alt		Range	c-nCstCo's SN, BC
F DR 03		Family	```DRYOPTERIDACEAE

Name	Rock Sword Fern
Genus	*Polystichum munitum var inbricans*
Occur	O	Origin	Native	Age	p	Reference	z62
Alias	Contorted frond *Polystichum munitum ssp nudatum (Munz)*
Alt		Range	c-nCstCo, sCa-BC
F DR 04		Family	```DRYOPTERIDACEAE

Name	California Polypody Fern
Genus	*Polypodium californicum*
Occur	C	Origin	Native	Age	p	Reference	g28 z58
Alias	1Pinn No indusia *Polyp californicum v.kaulf / v.parsonsiae / v.branscombii*
Alt		Range	c-nCstCo"s wStates -BC
F PO 01		Family	```POLYPODIACEAE

F 4

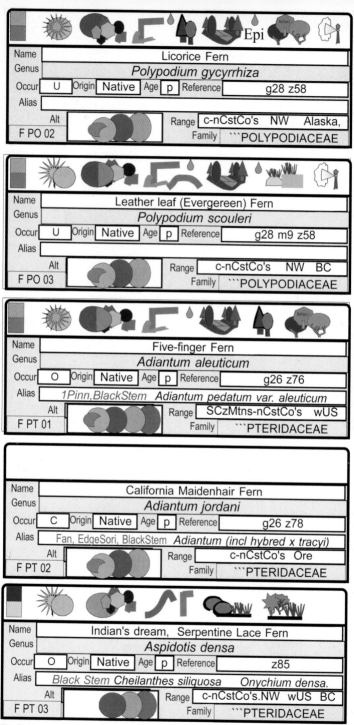

Licorice Fern

Name	Licorice Fern	
Genus	*Polypodium gycyrrhiza*	
Occur	U Origin Native Age p Reference	g28 z58
Alias		
Alt	Range	c-nCstCo's NW Alaska,
F PO 02	Family	```POLYPODIACEAE

Leather leaf (Evergereen) Fern

Name	Leather leaf (Evergereen) Fern	
Genus	*Polypodium scouleri*	
Occur	U Origin Native Age p Reference	g28 m9 z58
Alias		
Alt	Range	c-nCstCo's NW BC
F PO 03	Family	```POLYPODIACEAE

Five-finger Fern

Name	Five-finger Fern	
Genus	*Adiantum aleuticum*	
Occur	O Origin Native Age p Reference	g26 z76
Alias	*1Pinn,BlackStem Adiantum pedatum var. aleuticum*	
Alt	Range	SCzMtns-nCstCo's wUS
F PT 01	Family	```PTERIDACEAE

California Maidenhair Fern

Name	California Maidenhair Fern	
Genus	*Adiantum jordani*	
Occur	C Origin Native Age p Reference	g26 z78
Alias	Fan, EdgeSori, BlackStem *Adiantum (incl hybred x tracyi)*	
Alt	Range	c-nCstCo's Ore
F PT 02	Family	```PTERIDACEAE

Indian's dream, Serpentine Lace Fern

Name	Indian's dream, Serpentine Lace Fern	
Genus	*Aspidotis densa*	
Occur	O Origin Native Age p Reference	z85
Alias	*Black Stem Cheilanthes siliquosa Onychium densa.*	
Alt	Range	c-nCstCo's.NW wUS BC
F PT 03	Family	```PTERIDACEAE

F 6

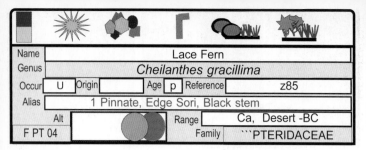

Name	Lace Fern
Genus	*Cheilanthes gracillima*
Occur	U	Origin		Age	p	Reference	z85
Alias	1 Pinnate, Edge Sori, Black stem
Alt		Range	Ca, Desert -BC
F PT 04		Family	```PTERIDACEAE

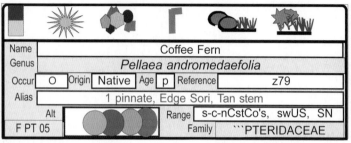

Name	Coffee Fern
Genus	*Pellaea andromedaefolia*
Occur	O	Origin	Native	Age	p	Reference	z79
Alias	1 pinnate, Edge Sori, Tan stem
Alt		Range	s-c-nCstCo's, swUS, SN
F PT 05		Family	```PTERIDACEAE

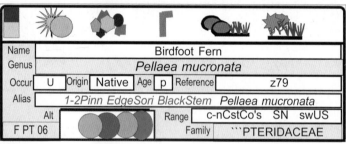

Name	Birdfoot Fern
Genus	*Pellaea mucronata*
Occur	U	Origin	Native	Age	p	Reference	z79
Alias	*1-2Pinn EdgeSori BlackStem Pellaea mucronata*
Alt		Range	c-nCstCo's SN swUS
F PT 06		Family	```PTERIDACEAE

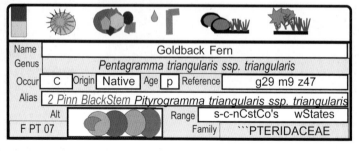

Name	Goldback Fern
Genus	*Pentagramma triangularis ssp. triangularis*
Occur	C	Origin	Native	Age	p	Reference	g29 m9 z47
Alias	*2 Pinn BlackStem Pityrogramma triangularis ssp. triangularis*
Alt		Range	s-c-nCstCo's wStates
F PT 07		Family	```PTERIDACEAE

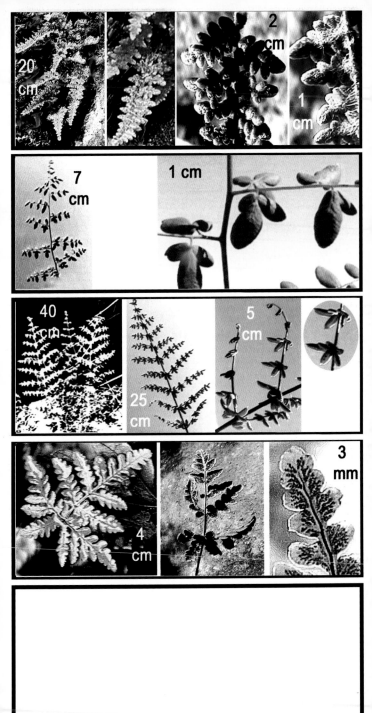

Gymnosperms

(Naked seed plants)

Cone bearing woody plants

Name	Gowen Cypress	
Genus	*Cupressus goveniana ssp goveniana*	
Occur	U — Origin: Native — Age: t — Reference	w24
Alias	Lack a long terminal shoot	
Alt	Range	nCalCst (MendicinoCo)
G Cu 01	Family	``CUPERACEAE

Name	Pigmy Forest (Mendocino) Cypress	
Genus	*Cupressus goveniana ssp pigmaea*	
Occur	R — Origin: Native — Age: t — Reference	
Alias	With a long terminal shoot *Cupressus pigmaea*	
Alt	Range	nCa(MendicinoCo, Pygmy F
G Cu 02	Family	``CUPERACEAE

Pygmy Forest

Name	Monterey Cypress	
Genus	*Cupressus macrocarpa*	
Occur	C — Origin: Native — Age: T — Reference	m108 w29
Alias		
Alt	Range	CstBigSur-MarinCo
G Cu 03	Family	``CUPERACEAE

Name	Sargent Cypress	
Genus	*Cupressus sargentii*	
Occur	R — Origin: Native — Age: t T — Reference	
Alias		
Alt	Range	SCz-Mendicino Ridges
G Cu 04	Family	``CUPERACEAE

G 2

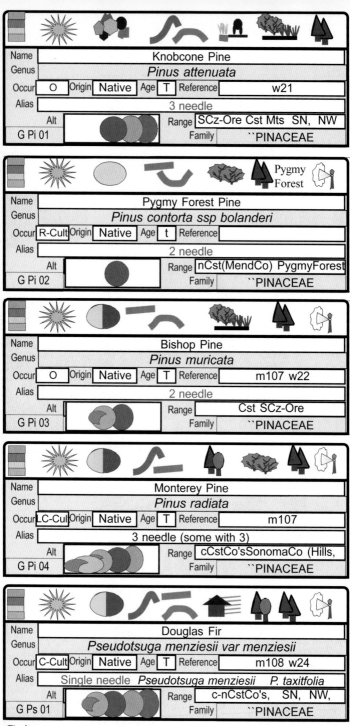

Name	Knobcone Pine					
Genus	*Pinus attenuata*					
Occur	O	Origin	Native	Age	T	Reference	w21
Alias	3 needle					
Alt		Range	SCz-Ore Cst Mts SN, NW			
G Pi 01		Family	``PINACEAE			

Name	Pygmy Forest Pine					
Genus	*Pinus contorta ssp bolanderi*					
Occur	R-Cult	Origin	Native	Age	t	Reference	
Alias	2 needle					
Alt		Range	nCst(MendCo) PygmyForest			
G Pi 02		Family	``PINACEAE			

Pygmy Forest

Name	Bishop Pine					
Genus	*Pinus muricata*					
Occur	O	Origin	Native	Age	T	Reference	m107 w22
Alias	2 needle					
Alt		Range	Cst SCz-Ore			
G Pi 03		Family	``PINACEAE			

Name	Monterey Pine					
Genus	*Pinus radiata*					
Occur	LC-Cult	Origin	Native	Age	T	Reference	m107
Alias	3 needle (some with 3)					
Alt		Range	cCstCo'sSonomaCo (Hills,			
G Pi 04		Family	``PINACEAE			

Name	Douglas Fir					
Genus	*Pseudotsuga menziesii var menziesii*					
Occur	C-Cult	Origin	Native	Age	T	Reference	m108 w24
Alias	Single needle *Pseudotsuga menziesii P. taxitfolia*					
Alt		Range	c-nCstCo's, SN, NW,			
G Ps 01		Family	``PINACEAE			

G 4

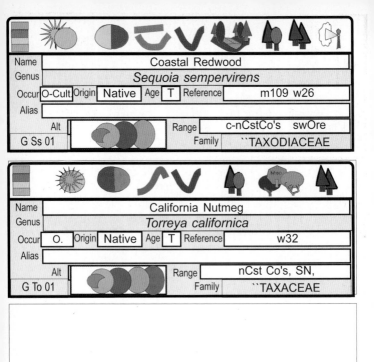

Name	Coastal Redwood
Genus	*Sequoia sempervirens*
Occur	O-Cult	Origin	Native	Age	T	Reference	m109 w26
Alias	
Alt		Range	c-nCstCo's swOre
G Ss 01		Family	``TAXODIACEAE

Name	California Nutmeg
Genus	*Torreya californica*
Occur	O.	Origin	Native	Age	T	Reference	w32
Alias	
Alt		Range	nCst Co's, SN,
G To 01		Family	``TAXACEAE

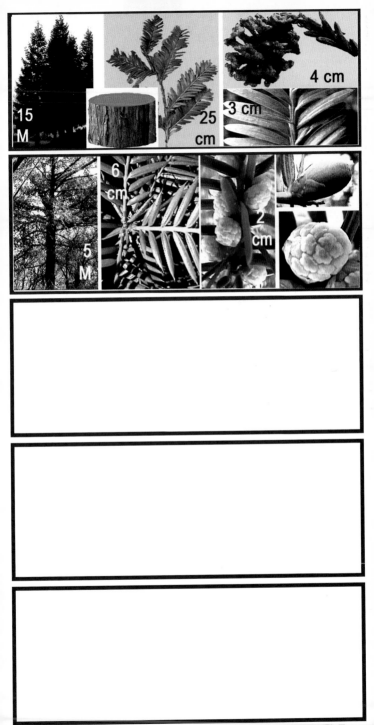

Monocots

Flower parts generally in grops or multiples of 3
Parallel vein leaves
Stem or Pedicel with vascular bundles scattered
throughout the core

Name	Curved Coralla Montbretia
Genus	*Chasmanthe floribunda*

Occur	O-Exc	Origin	sAfr	Age	p	Reference	

Alias	*Chasmanthe aethiopica*

Alt		Range	c-nCstCo"s, Ore
M IR 01		Family	`IRIDACEAE

Name	Douglas Iris
Genus	*Iris douglasiana*

Occur	C	Origin	Native	Age	p	Reference	e75 n126

Alias	*Iris douglasiana var, major*

Alt		Range	c-nCstCo"s, Ore
M IR 02		Family	`IRIDACEAE

Name	Ferdaldi's Iris
Genus	*Iris fernaldii*

Occur	o	Origin	Native	Age	p	Reference	n126

Alias	

Alt		Range	BigSur-SCzMts
M IR 03		Family	`IRIDACEAE

Name	Coastal Iris
Genus	*Iris longipetala*

Occur	C	Origin	Native	Age	p	Reference	e75 n350 s58

Alias	

Alt		Range	Big Sur-Mendi (OuterMtns)
M IR 04		Family	`IRIDACEAE

M 2

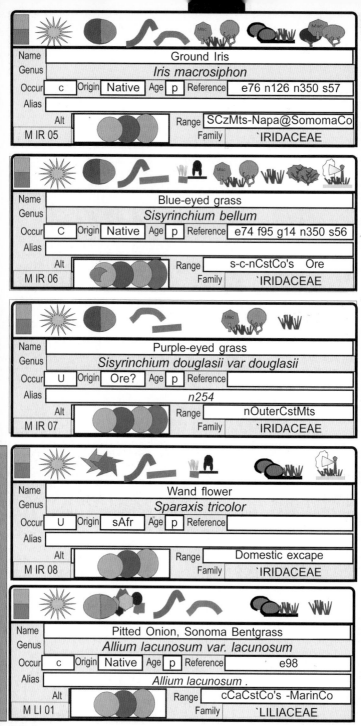

Name	Ground Iris
Genus	*Iris macrosiphon*
Occur	c · Origin Native · Age p · Reference e76 n126 n350 s57
Alias	
Alt	Range SCzMts-Napa@SomomaCo
M IR 05	Family `IRIDACEAE

Name	Blue-eyed grass
Genus	*Sisyrinchium bellum*
Occur	C · Origin Native · Age p · Reference e74 f95 g14 n350 s56
Alias	
Alt	Range s-c-nCstCo's Ore
M IR 06	Family `IRIDACEAE

Name	Purple-eyed grass
Genus	*Sisyrinchium douglasii var douglasii*
Occur	U · Origin Ore? · Age p · Reference
Alias	n254
Alt	Range nOuterCstMts
M IR 07	Family `IRIDACEAE

Name	Wand flower
Genus	*Sparaxis tricolor*
Occur	U · Origin sAfr · Age p · Reference
Alias	
Alt	Range Domestic excape
M IR 08	Family `IRIDACEAE

Name	Pitted Onion, Sonoma Bentgrass
Genus	*Allium lacunosum var. lacunosum*
Occur	c · Origin Native · Age p · Reference e98
Alias	*Allium lacunosum .*
Alt	Range cCaCstCo's -MarinCo
M LI 01	Family `LILIACEAE

M 4

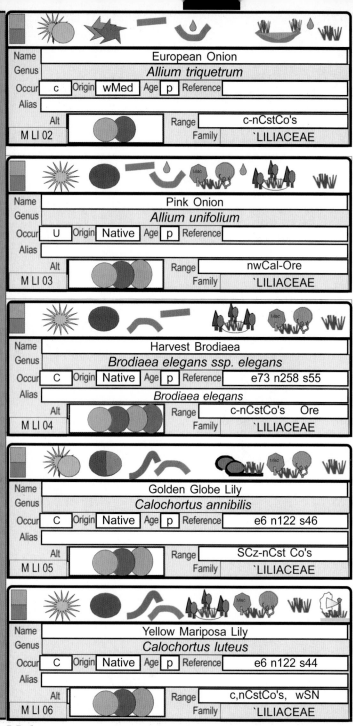

Name	European Onion
Genus	*Allium triquetrum*
Occur	c Origin wMed Age p Reference
Alias	
Alt	Range c-nCstCo's
M Ll 02	Family `LILIACEAE

Name	Pink Onion
Genus	*Allium unifolium*
Occur	U Origin Native Age p Reference
Alias	
Alt	Range nwCal-Ore
M Ll 03	Family `LILIACEAE

Name	Harvest Brodiaea
Genus	*Brodiaea elegans ssp. elegans*
Occur	C Origin Native Age p Reference e73 n258 s55
Alias	*Brodiaea elegans*
Alt	Range c-nCstCo's Ore
M Ll 04	Family `LILIACEAE

Name	Golden Globe Lily
Genus	*Calochortus annibilis*
Occur	C Origin Native Age p Reference e6 n122 s46
Alias	
Alt	Range SCz-nCst Co's
M Ll 05	Family `LILIACEAE

Name	Yellow Mariposa Lily
Genus	*Calochortus luteus*
Occur	C Origin Native Age p Reference e6 n122 s44
Alias	
Alt	Range c,nCstCo's, wSN
M Ll 06	Family `LILIACEAE

M 6

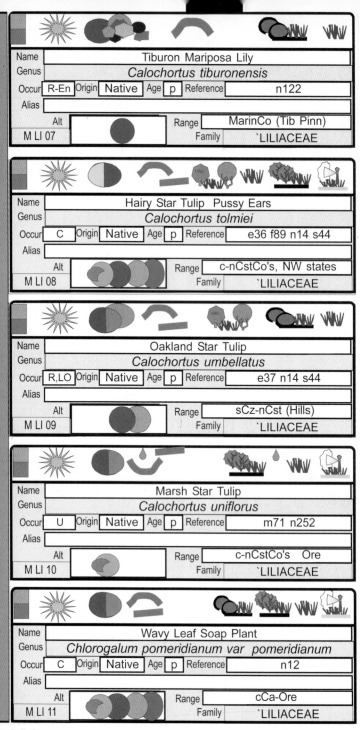

Name	Tiburon Mariposa Lily
Genus	*Calochortus tiburonensis*
Occur	R-En Origin Native Age p Reference n122
Alias	
Alt	Range MarinCo (Tib Pinn)
M LI 07	Family `LILIACEAE

Name	Hairy Star Tulip Pussy Ears
Genus	*Calochortus tolmiei*
Occur	C Origin Native Age p Reference e36 f89 n14 s44
Alias	
Alt	Range c-nCstCo's, NW states
M LI 08	Family `LILIACEAE

Name	Oakland Star Tulip
Genus	*Calochortus umbellatus*
Occur	R,LO Origin Native Age p Reference e37 n14 s44
Alias	
Alt	Range sCz-nCst (Hills)
M LI 09	Family `LILIACEAE

Name	Marsh Star Tulip
Genus	*Calochortus uniflorus*
Occur	U Origin Native Age p Reference m71 n252
Alias	
Alt	Range c-nCstCo's Ore
M LI 10	Family `LILIACEAE

Name	Wavy Leaf Soap Plant
Genus	*Chlorogalum pomeridianum var pomeridianum*
Occur	C Origin Native Age p Reference n12
Alias	
Alt	Range cCa-Ore
M LI 11	Family `LILIACEAE

M 8

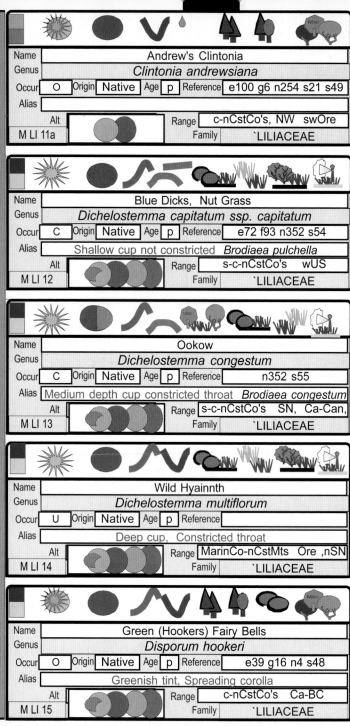

Name	Andrew's Clintonia
Genus	*Clintonia andrewsiana*
Occur	O	Origin	Native	Age	p	Reference	e100 g6 n254 s21 s49
Alias	
Alt		Range	c-nCstCo's, NW swOre
M LI 11a		Family	`LILIACEAE

Name	Blue Dicks, Nut Grass
Genus	*Dichelostemma capitatum ssp. capitatum*
Occur	C	Origin	Native	Age	p	Reference	e72 f93 n352 s54
Alias	Shallow cup not constricted *Brodiaea pulchella*
Alt		Range	s-c-nCstCo's wUS
M LI 12		Family	`LILIACEAE

Name	Ookow
Genus	*Dichelostemma congestum*
Occur	C	Origin	Native	Age	p	Reference	n352 s55
Alias	Medium depth cup constricted throat *Brodiaea congestum*
Alt		Range	s-c-nCstCo's SN, Ca-Can,
M LI 13		Family	`LILIACEAE

Name	Wild Hyainnth
Genus	*Dichelostemma multiflorum*
Occur	U	Origin	Native	Age	p	Reference	
Alias	Deep cup, Constricted throat
Alt		Range	MarinCo-nCstMts Ore ,nSN
M LI 14		Family	`LILIACEAE

Name	Green (Hookers) Fairy Bells
Genus	*Disporum hookeri*
Occur	O	Origin	Native	Age	p	Reference	e39 g16 n4 s48
Alias	Greenish tint, Spreading corolla
Alt		Range	c-nCstCo's Ca-BC
M LI 15		Family	`LILIACEAE

M 10

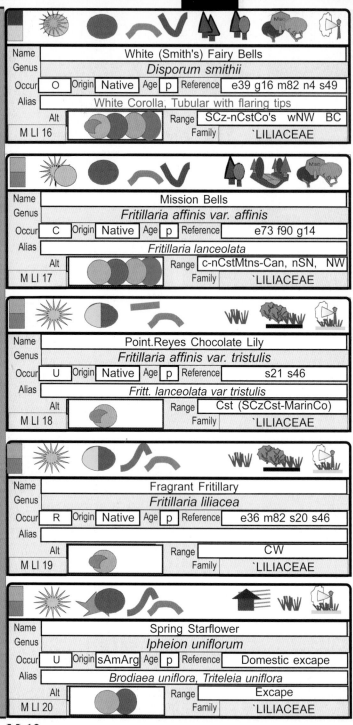

White (Smith's) Fairy Bells

Name	White (Smith's) Fairy Bells
Genus	*Disporum smithii*
Occur	O	Origin	Native	Age	p	Reference	e39 g16 m82 n4 s49
Alias	White Corolla, Tubular with flaring tips
Alt		Range	SCz-nCstCo's wNW BC
M LI 16		Family	`LILIACEAE

Mission Bells

Name	Mission Bells
Genus	*Fritillaria affinis var. affinis*
Occur	C	Origin	Native	Age	p	Reference	e73 f90 g14
Alias	*Fritillaria lanceolata*
Alt		Range	c-nCstMtns-Can, nSN, NW
M LI 17		Family	`LILIACEAE

Point.Reyes Chocolate Lily

Name	Point.Reyes Chocolate Lily
Genus	*Fritillaria affinis var. tristulis*
Occur	U	Origin	Native	Age	p	Reference	s21 s46
Alias	*Fritt. lanceolata var tristulis*
Alt		Range	Cst (SCzCst-MarinCo)
M LI 18		Family	`LILIACEAE

Fragrant Fritillary

Name	Fragrant Fritillary
Genus	*Fritillaria liliacea*
Occur	R	Origin	Native	Age	p	Reference	e36 m82 s20 s46
Alias	
Alt		Range	CW
M LI 19		Family	`LILIACEAE

Spring Starflower

Name	Spring Starflower
Genus	*Ipheion uniflorum*
Occur	U	Origin	sAmArg	Age	p	Reference	Domestic excape
Alias	*Brodiaea uniflora, Triteleia uniflora*
Alt		Range	Excape
M LI 20		Family	`LILIACEAE

M 12

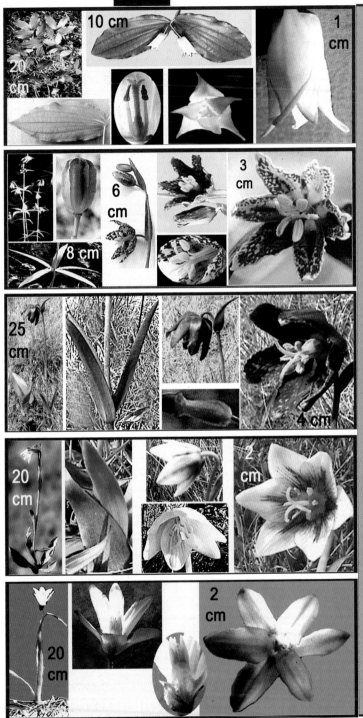

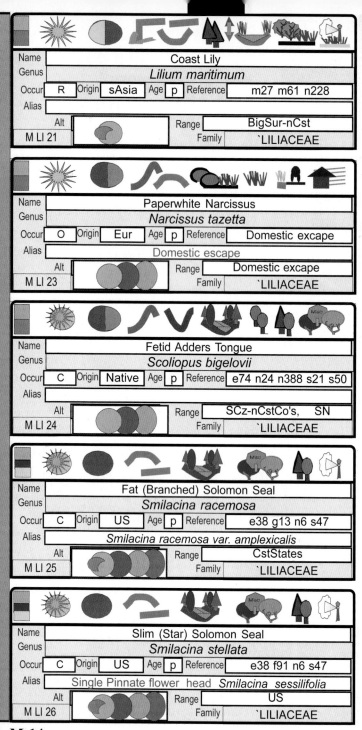

Name	Coast Lily
Genus	*Lilium maritimum*
Occur	R
Origin	sAsia
Age	p
Reference	m27 m61 n228
Alias	
Alt	
Range	BigSur-nCst
M LI 21	
Family	`LILIACEAE

Name	Paperwhite Narcissus
Genus	*Narcissus tazetta*
Occur	O
Origin	Eur
Age	p
Reference	Domestic excape
Alias	Domestic escape
Alt	
Range	Domestic excape
M LI 23	
Family	`LILIACEAE

Name	Fetid Adders Tongue
Genus	*Scoliopus bigelovii*
Occur	C
Origin	Native
Age	p
Reference	e74 n24 n388 s21 s50
Alias	
Alt	
Range	SCz-nCstCo's, SN
M LI 24	
Family	`LILIACEAE

Name	Fat (Branched) Solomon Seal
Genus	*Smilacina racemosa*
Occur	C
Origin	US
Age	p
Reference	e38 g13 n6 s47
Alias	*Smilacina racemosa var. amplexicalis*
Alt	
Range	CstStates
M LI 25	
Family	`LILIACEAE

Name	Slim (Star) Solomon Seal
Genus	*Smilacina stellata*
Occur	C
Origin	US
Age	p
Reference	e38 f91 n6 s47
Alias	Single Pinnate flower head *Smilacina sessilifolia*
Alt	
Range	US
M LI 26	
Family	`LILIACEAE

M 14

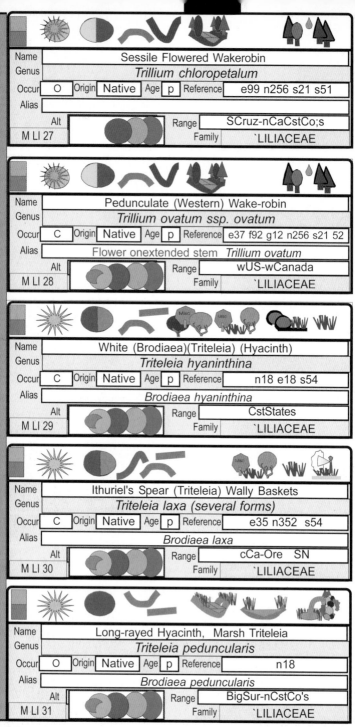

Name Sessile Flowered Wakerobin
Genus *Trillium chloropetalum*
Occur O | **Origin** Native | **Age** p | **Reference** e99 n256 s21 s51
Alias
Alt | **Range** SCruz-nCaCstCo;s
M Ll 27 | **Family** `LILIACEAE

Name Pedunculate (Western) Wake-robin
Genus *Trillium ovatum ssp. ovatum*
Occur C | **Origin** Native | **Age** p | **Reference** e37 f92 g12 n256 s21 52
Alias Flower onextended stem *Trillium ovatum*
Alt | **Range** wUS-wCanada
M Ll 28 | **Family** `LILIACEAE

Name White (Brodiaea)(Triteleia) (Hyacinth)
Genus *Triteleia hyaninthina*
Occur C | **Origin** Native | **Age** p | **Reference** n18 e18 s54
Alias *Brodiaea hyaninthina*
Alt | **Range** CstStates
M Ll 29 | **Family** `LILIACEAE

Name Ithuriel's Spear (Triteleia) Wally Baskets
Genus *Triteleia laxa (several forms)*
Occur C | **Origin** Native | **Age** p | **Reference** e35 n352 s54
Alias *Brodiaea laxa*
Alt | **Range** cCa-Ore SN
M Ll 30 | **Family** `LILIACEAE

Name Long-rayed Hyacinth, Marsh Triteleia
Genus *Triteleia peduncularis*
Occur O | **Origin** Native | **Age** p | **Reference** n18
Alias *Brodiaea peduncularis*
Alt | **Range** BigSur-nCstCo's
M Ll 31 | **Family** `LILIACEAE

M 16

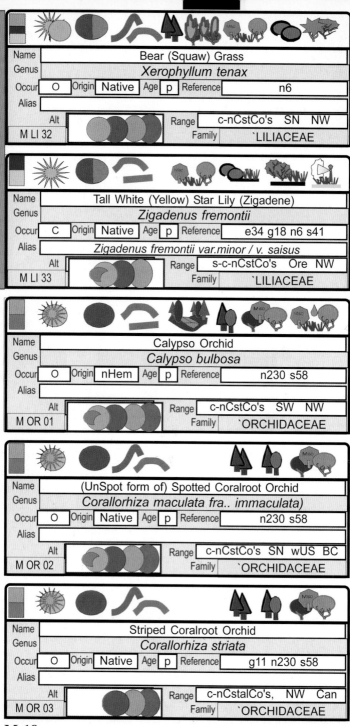

Name	Bear (Squaw) Grass				
Genus	*Xerophyllum tenax*				
Occur	O	Origin	Native	Age	p	Reference	n6
Alias					
Alt			Range	c-nCstCo's SN NW
M LI 32			Family	`LILIACEAE

Name	Tall White (Yellow) Star Lily (Zigadene)				
Genus	*Zigadenus fremontii*				
Occur	C	Origin	Native	Age	p	Reference	e34 g18 n6 s41
Alias	*Zigadenus fremontii var.minor / v. saisus*				
Alt			Range	s-c-nCstCo's Ore NW
M LI 33			Family	`LILIACEAE

Name	Calypso Orchid				
Genus	*Calypso bulbosa*				
Occur	O	Origin	nHem	Age	p	Reference	n230 s58
Alias					
Alt			Range	c-nCstCo's SW NW
M OR 01			Family	`ORCHIDACEAE

Name	(UnSpot form of) Spotted Coralroot Orchid				
Genus	*Corallorhiza maculata fra.. immaculata)*				
Occur	O	Origin	Native	Age	p	Reference	n230 s58
Alias					
Alt			Range	c-nCstCo's SN wUS BC
M OR 02			Family	`ORCHIDACEAE

Name	Striped Coralroot Orchid				
Genus	*Corallorhiza striata*				
Occur	O	Origin	Native	Age	p	Reference	g11 n230 s58
Alias					
Alt			Range	c-nCstalCo's, NW Can
M OR 03			Family	`ORCHIDACEAE

M 18

Common but does not flower locally

Sawtooth edge

CYPERACEAE (Sedge Family)

Carex globosa
Round fruited sedge

Carex nudata   Sedge

Scirpus californicus
California Tule

Carex sp.

Cyperum eragrostis Umbrella Tule Cyperum strigosus False Nutsedge

JUNCAGINACEAE (Arrow-Grass Family)

Triglochin maritima   Sea Shore Arrow Grass

JUNCACEAE (Rushes)

Juncus bolanderi   Clustered Rush

Juncus capitatus
Annual Roundedheaded Rush

Juncus covillei
Long fruited rush

20 cm

2 cm

1 cm

Juncus effusus var brunneus   Inland Rush

1 cm

1 cm

Juncus occidentalis   Western Rush

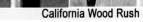

Luzula comosa   California Wood Rush

POACEAE (Grass Family)

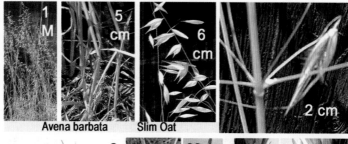

Avena barbata Slim Oat

Ammonpila arenaria European Beach Grass

Briza maxima Rattlesnake Grass

Briza minor

Little Rattlesnake Grass

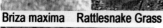

Bromus diandrus Rip Gut Brome

Dactylis glomerata Orchard grass

Cortaderia scolloana Pampas Grass

Cynosurus echinatus

Dogtail Grass

M 22

POACEAE (Grass Family)

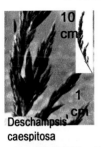

Deschampsis
caespitosa

Festuca californica

California Festuca

Elymus californica

Bottlebrush Grass

Elymus multisetus   Big Squirrel Tail Grass

Holcus lanatus   Velvet Grass

Barley
(Foxtail?)
Grass

*Hordium
murinum
(perhaps)*

Melica californica
California Melic

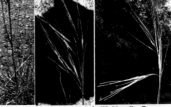

Nasella lepida (pokera) Calif. Needle Grass

M 23

POACEAE (Grass Family)

Panicum sp

Phalaris aquatica   Harding grass

Polypogon monospeliensis Bearded Grass

Spartina foliosa   Cord Grass

THYPHACEAE Horsetail Family

2 M

40 cm

Typha augustifolia   Narrow Leaf Cattail

2 M

15 cm

30 cm

Typha latifolia   Wide Leaf Horsetail

Woody DicotTrees bushes
and Vines
W 2----W39

Major Indexed Herbaceous
Dicot Families
x1---x111

Smaller Non Indexed
Herbaceous Dicot Families
x112--x133

Woody Dicot Trees, Bushes and Vines

Dicot trees generally spread from a single major trunk. Bushes generally divide into multiple smaller trunks or branches less then a meter from the ground. this book will consider any woody plant more then 2.5 meters tall to be a tree regardless of its branching pattern.

Name	*Big Leaf Maple					
Genus	*Acer macrophyllum*					
Occur	C	Origin	Native	Age	t T	Reference	m111 w57
Alias						
Alt				Range	c-nCstCo's wCst States	
T AC 01				Family	ACERACEAE	

Name	Blue Elderberry					
Genus	*Sambucus mexicana*					
Occur	C	Origin	Native	Age	t	Reference	f76 w61
Alias	CAPRI Fam Sambucus glauca					
Alt				Range	s-c-nCstCo's wStates,	
T AD 02				Family	ADOXACEAE	

Name	California (Peru) Pepper Tree					
Genus	*Schinum molle*					
Occur	O	Origin	Peru	Age	T	Reference	
Alias						
Alt				Range	s-cCal, SW SAmer	
T AN 02				Family	ANACARDIACEAE	

Name	White Alder					
Genus	*Alnus rhombifolia*					
Occur	C	Origin	Native	Age	T	Reference	m110 w48
Alias						
Alt				Range	Ca, wStates	
T BE 11				Family	BETULACEAE	

Some low bushes such as Iceplant have a rubbery wood and others could be discribed as a tree but in adult form are less then 2.5 meters tall. this book will discribe them in the bush and vine sections (V).

If in doubt check both T(Tree) and V(Bush,Vine) sections

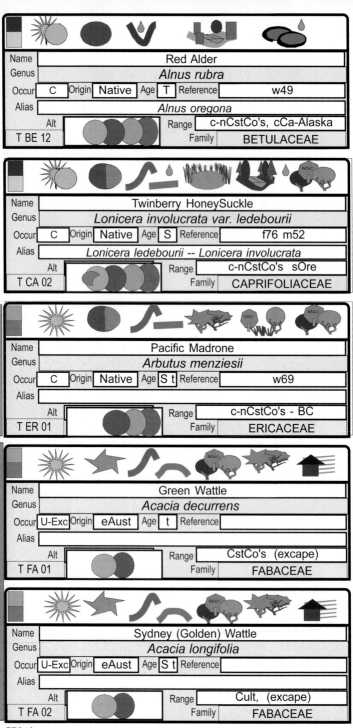

Red Alder

Name	Red Alder
Genus	*Alnus rubra*
Occur	C · Origin Native · Age T · Reference w49
Alias	*Alnus oregona*
Alt	Range c-nCstCo's, cCa-Alaska
T BE 12	Family BETULACEAE

Twinberry HoneySuckle

Name	Twinberry HoneySuckle
Genus	*Lonicera involucrata var. ledebourii*
Occur	C · Origin Native · Age S · Reference f76 m52
Alias	*Lonicera ledebourii -- Lonicera involucrata*
Alt	Range c-nCstCo's sOre
T CA 02	Family CAPRIFOLIACEAE

Pacific Madrone

Name	Pacific Madrone
Genus	*Arbutus menziesii*
Occur	C · Origin Native · Age S t · Reference w69
Alias	
Alt	Range c-nCstCo's - BC
T ER 01	Family ERICACEAE

Green Wattle

Name	Green Wattle
Genus	*Acacia decurrens*
Occur	U-Exc · Origin eAust · Age t · Reference
Alias	
Alt	Range CstCo's (excape)
T FA 01	Family FABACEAE

Sydney (Golden) Wattle

Name	Sydney (Golden) Wattle
Genus	*Acacia longifolia*
Occur	U-Exc · Origin eAust · Age S t · Reference
Alias	
Alt	Range Cult, (excape)
T FA 02	Family FABACEAE

W 4

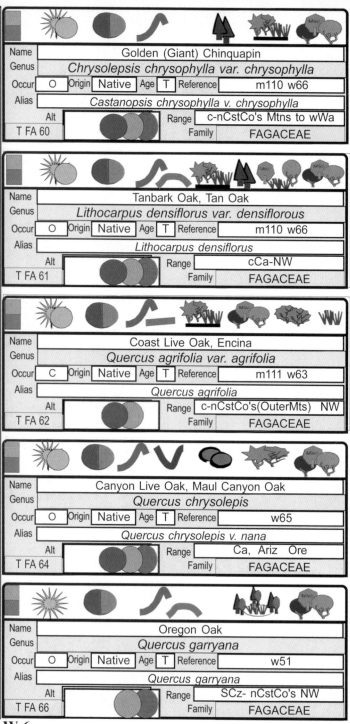

Name Golden (Giant) Chinquapin

Genus *Chrysolepis chrysophylla var. chrysophylla*

Occur O **Origin** Native **Age** T **Reference** m110 w66

Alias *Castanopsis chrysophylla v. chrysophylla*

Alt | **Range** c-nCstCo's Mtns to wWa

T FA 60 | **Family** FAGACEAE

Name Tanbark Oak, Tan Oak

Genus *Lithocarpus densiflorus var. densiflorous*

Occur O **Origin** Native **Age** T **Reference** m110 w66

Alias *Lithocarpus densiflorus*

Alt | **Range** cCa-NW

T FA 61 | **Family** FAGACEAE

Name Coast Live Oak, Encina

Genus *Quercus agrifolia var. agrifolia*

Occur C **Origin** Native **Age** T **Reference** m111 w63

Alias *Quercus agrifolia*

Alt | **Range** c-nCstCo's(OuterMts) NW

T FA 62 | **Family** FAGACEAE

Name Canyon Live Oak, Maul Canyon Oak

Genus *Quercus chrysolepis*

Occur O **Origin** Native **Age** T **Reference** w65

Alias *Quercus chrysolepis v. nana*

Alt | **Range** Ca, Ariz Ore

T FA 64 | **Family** FAGACEAE

Name Oregon Oak

Genus *Quercus garryana*

Occur O **Origin** Native **Age** T **Reference** w51

Alias *Quercus garryana*

Alt | **Range** SCz- nCstCo's NW

T FA 66 | **Family** FAGACEAE

W 6

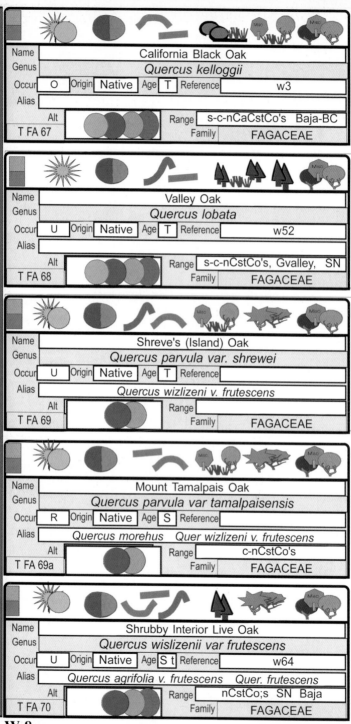

Name	California Black Oak
Genus	*Quercus kelloggii*
Occur	O	Origin	Native	Age	T	Reference	w3
Alias	
Alt		Range	s-c-nCaCstCo's Baja-BC
T FA 67		Family	FAGACEAE

Name	Valley Oak
Genus	*Quercus lobata*
Occur	U	Origin	Native	Age	T	Reference	w52
Alias	
Alt		Range	s-c-nCstCo's, Gvalley, SN
T FA 68		Family	FAGACEAE

Name	Shreve's (Island) Oak
Genus	*Quercus parvula var. shrewei*
Occur	U	Origin	Native	Age	T	Reference	
Alias	*Quercus wizlizeni v. frutescens*
Alt		Range	
T FA 69		Family	FAGACEAE

Name	Mount Tamalpais Oak
Genus	*Quercus parvula var tamalpaisensis*
Occur	R	Origin	Native	Age	S	Reference	
Alias	*Quercus morehus Quer wizlizeni v. frutescens*
Alt		Range	c-nCstCo's
T FA 69a		Family	FAGACEAE

Name	Shrubby Interior Live Oak
Genus	*Quercus wislizenii var frutescens*
Occur	U	Origin	Native	Age	S t	Reference	w64
Alias	*Quercus agrifolia v. frutescens Quer. frutescens*
Alt		Range	nCstCo;s SN Baja
T FA 70		Family	FAGACEAE

W 8

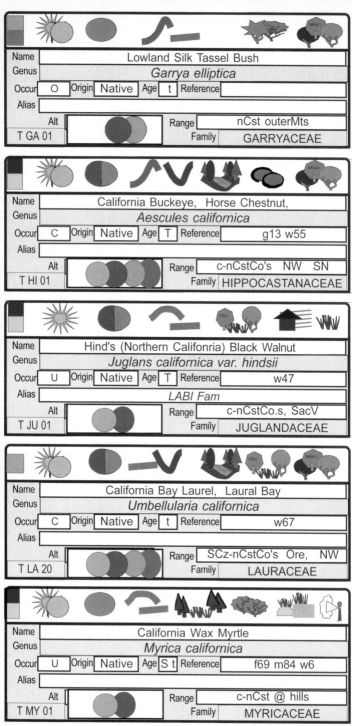

Name	Lowland Silk Tassel Bush				
Genus	*Garrya elliptica*				
Occur	O	**Origin** Native	**Age** t	**Reference**	
Alias					
Alt			**Range**	nCst outerMts	
T GA 01			**Family**	GARRYACEAE	

Name	California Buckeye, Horse Chestnut,				
Genus	*Aescules californica*				
Occur	C	**Origin** Native	**Age** T	**Reference**	g13 w55
Alias					
Alt			**Range**	c-nCstCo's NW SN	
T HI 01			**Family**	HIPPOCASTANACEAE	

Name	Hind's (Northern Califonria) Black Walnut				
Genus	*Juglans californica var. hindsii*				
Occur	U	**Origin** Native	**Age** T	**Reference**	w47
Alias		*LABI Fam*			
Alt			**Range**	c-nCstCo.s, SacV	
T JU 01			**Family**	JUGLANDACEAE	

Name	California Bay Laurel, Laural Bay				
Genus	*Umbellularia californica*				
Occur	C	**Origin** Native	**Age** t	**Reference**	w67
Alias					
Alt			**Range**	SCz-nCstCo's Ore, NW	
T LA 20			**Family**	LAURACEAE	

Name	California Wax Myrtle				
Genus	*Myrica californica*				
Occur	U	**Origin** Native	**Age** S t	**Reference**	f69 m84 w6
Alias					
Alt			**Range**	c-nCst @ hills	
T MY 01			**Family**	MYRICACEAE	

W 10

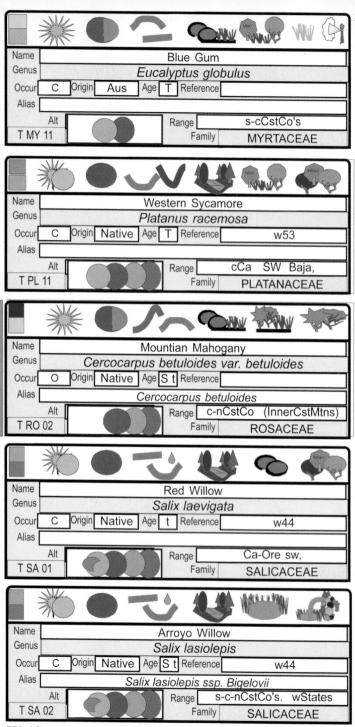

Name Blue Gum
Genus *Eucalyptus globulus*
Occur C **Origin** Aus **Age** T **Reference**
Alias
Alt
T MY 11 **Range** s-cCstCo's
Family MYRTACEAE

Name Western Sycamore
Genus *Platanus racemosa*
Occur C **Origin** Native **Age** T **Reference** w53
Alias
Alt
T PL 11 **Range** cCa SW Baja,
Family PLATANACEAE

Name Mountian Mahogany
Genus *Cercocarpus betuloides var. betuloides*
Occur O **Origin** Native **Age** S t **Reference**
Alias *Cercocarpus betuloides*
Alt
T RO 02 **Range** c-nCstCo (InnerCstMtns)
Family ROSACEAE

Name Red Willow
Genus *Salix laevigata*
Occur C **Origin** Native **Age** t **Reference** w44
Alias
Alt
T SA 01 **Range** Ca-Ore sw,
Family SALICACEAE

Name Arroyo Willow
Genus *Salix lasiolepis*
Occur C **Origin** Native **Age** S t **Reference** w44
Alias *Salix lasiolepis ssp. Bigelovii*
Alt
T SA 02 **Range** s-c-nCstCo's. wStates
Family SALICACEAE

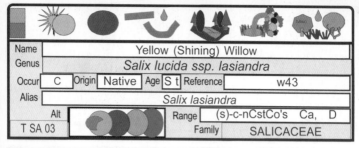

Name	Yellow (Shining) Willow				
Genus	*Salix lucida ssp. lasiandra*				
Occur	C	Origin	Native	Age	S t	Reference	w43
Alias	*Salix lasiandra*				
Alt		Range	(s)-c-nCstCo's Ca, D
T SA 03		Family	SALICACEAE

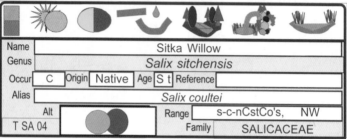

Name	Sitka Willow				
Genus	*Salix sitchensis*				
Occur	C	Origin	Native	Age	S t	Reference	
Alias	*Salix coultei*				
Alt		Range	s-c-nCstCo's, NW
T SA 04		Family	SALICACEAE

Bushes, Brush and Woody Vines

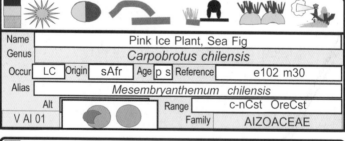

Name	Pink Ice Plant, Sea Fig				
Genus	*Carpobrotus chilensis*				
Occur	LC	Origin	sAfr	Age	p s	Reference	e102 m30
Alias	*Mesembryanthemum chilensis*				
Alt		Range	c-nCst OreCst
V AI 01		Family	AIZOACEAE

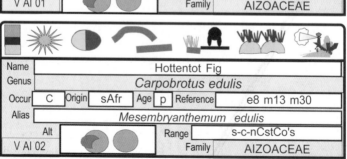

Name	Hottentot Fig				
Genus	*Carpobrotus edulis*				
Occur	C	Origin	sAfr	Age	p	Reference	e8 m13 m30
Alias	*Mesembryanthemum edulis*				
Alt		Range	s-c-nCstCo's
V AI 02		Family	AIZOACEAE

W 14

Some low bushes such as Iceplant have a rubbery wood and others could be discribed as a tree but in adult form are less then 2.5 meters tall. this book will discribe them in the bush and vine sections (V).

If in doubt check both T(Tree) and V(Bush,Vine) sections

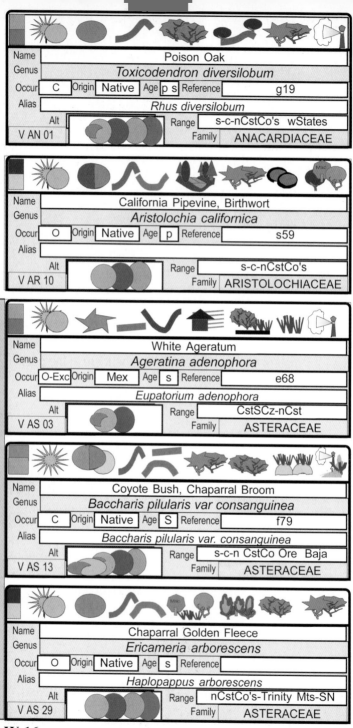

Name	Poison Oak
Genus	*Toxicodendron diversilobum*
Occur	C · Origin Native · Age p s · Reference g19
Alias	*Rhus diversilobum*
Alt	Range s-c-nCstCo's wStates
V AN 01	Family ANACARDIACEAE

Name	California Pipevine, Birthwort
Genus	*Aristolochia californica*
Occur	O · Origin Native · Age p · Reference s59
Alias	
Alt	Range s-c-nCstCo's
V AR 10	Family ARISTOLOCHIACEAE

Name	White Ageratum
Genus	*Ageratina adenophora*
Occur	O-Exc · Origin Mex · Age s · Reference e68
Alias	*Eupatorium adenophora*
Alt	Range CstSCz-nCst
V AS 03	Family ASTERACEAE

Name	Coyote Bush, Chaparral Broom
Genus	*Baccharis pilularis var consanguinea*
Occur	C · Origin Native · Age S · Reference f79
Alias	*Baccharis pilularis var. consanguinea*
Alt	Range s-c-n CstCo Ore Baja
V AS 13	Family ASTERACEAE

Name	Chaparral Golden Fleece
Genus	*Ericameria arborescens*
Occur	O · Origin Native · Age s · Reference
Alias	*Haplopappus arborescens*
Alt	Range nCstCo's-Trinity Mts-SN
V AS 29	Family ASTERACEAE

W 16

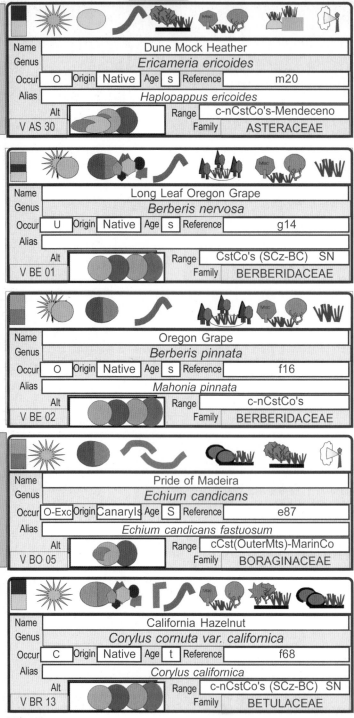

Name	Dune Mock Heather
Genus	*Ericameria ericoides*
Occur	O	Origin	Native	Age	s	Reference	m20
Alias	*Haplopappus ericoides*
Alt		Range	c-nCstCo's-Mendeceno
V AS 30		Family	ASTERACEAE

Name	Long Leaf Oregon Grape
Genus	*Berberis nervosa*
Occur	U	Origin	Native	Age	s	Reference	g14
Alias	
Alt		Range	CstCo's (SCz-BC) SN
V BE 01		Family	BERBERIDACEAE

Name	Oregon Grape
Genus	*Berberis pinnata*
Occur	O	Origin	Native	Age	s	Reference	f16
Alias	*Mahonia pinnata*
Alt		Range	c-nCstCo's
V BE 02		Family	BERBERIDACEAE

Name	Pride of Madeira
Genus	*Echium candicans*
Occur	O-Exc	Origin	CanaryIs	Age	S	Reference	e87
Alias	*Echium candicans fastuosum*
Alt		Range	cCst(OuterMts)-MarinCo
V BO 05		Family	BORAGINACEAE

Name	California Hazelnut
Genus	*Corylus cornuta var. californica*
Occur	C	Origin	Native	Age	t	Reference	f68
Alias	*Corylus californica*
Alt		Range	c-nNCstCo's (SCz-BC) SN
V BR 13		Family	BETULACEAE

W 18

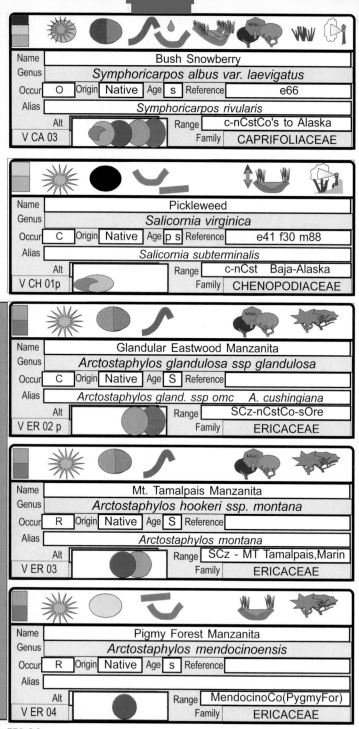

Name	Bush Snowberry
Genus	*Symphoricarpos albus var. laevigatus*
Occur	O	Origin	Native	Age	s	Reference	e66
Alias	*Symphoricarpos rivularis*
Alt		Range	c-nCstCo's to Alaska
V CA 03		Family	CAPRIFOLIACEAE

Name	Pickleweed
Genus	*Salicornia virginica*
Occur	C	Origin	Native	Age	p s	Reference	e41 f30 m88
Alias	*Salicornia subterminalis*
Alt		Range	c-nCst Baja-Alaska
V CH 01p		Family	CHENOPODIACEAE

Name	Glandular Eastwood Manzanita
Genus	*Arctostaphylos glandulosa ssp glandulosa*
Occur	C	Origin	Native	Age	S	Reference	
Alias	*Arctostaphylos gland. ssp omc A. cushingiana*
Alt		Range	SCz-nCstCo-sOre
V ER 02 p		Family	ERICACEAE

Name	Mt. Tamalpais Manzanita
Genus	*Arctostaphylos hookeri ssp. montana*
Occur	R	Origin	Native	Age	S	Reference	
Alias	*Arctostaphylos montana*
Alt		Range	SCz - MT Tamalpais,Marin
V ER 03		Family	ERICACEAE

Name	Pigmy Forest Manzanita
Genus	*Arctostaphylos mendocinoensis*
Occur	R	Origin	Native	Age	s	Reference	
Alias	
Alt		Range	MendocinoCo(PygmyFor)
V ER 04		Family	ERICACEAE

W 20

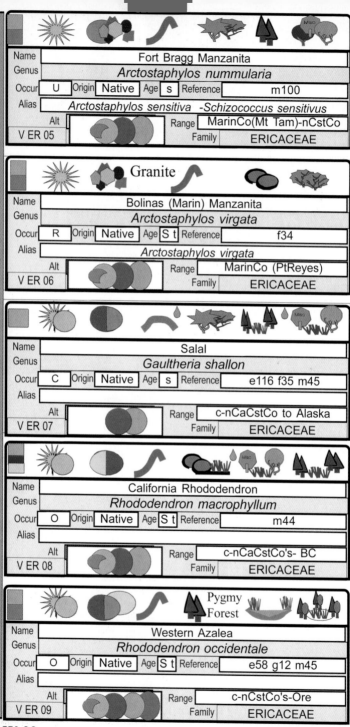

Name	Fort Bragg Manzanita
Genus	*Arctostaphylos nummularia*
Occur	U	Origin	Native	Age	s	Reference	m100
Alias	*Arctostaphylos sensitiva -Schizococcus sensitivus*
Alt		Range	MarinCo(Mt Tam)-nCstCo
V ER 05		Family	ERICACEAE

Granite

Name	Bolinas (Marin) Manzanita
Genus	*Arctostaphylos virgata*
Occur	R	Origin	Native	Age	S t	Reference	f34
Alias	*Arctostaphylos virgata*
Alt		Range	MarinCo (PtReyes)
V ER 06		Family	ERICACEAE

Name	Salal
Genus	*Gaultheria shallon*
Occur	C	Origin	Native	Age	s	Reference	e116 f35 m45
Alias	
Alt		Range	c-nCaCstCo to Alaska
V ER 07		Family	ERICACEAE

Name	California Rhododendron
Genus	*Rhododendron macrophyllum*
Occur	O	Origin	Native	Age	S t	Reference	m44
Alias	
Alt		Range	c-nCaCstCo's- BC
V ER 08		Family	ERICACEAE

Pygmy Forest

Name	Western Azalea
Genus	*Rhododendron occidentale*
Occur	O	Origin	Native	Age	S t	Reference	e58 g12 m45
Alias	
Alt		Range	c-nCstCo's-Ore
V ER 09		Family	ERICACEAE

W 22

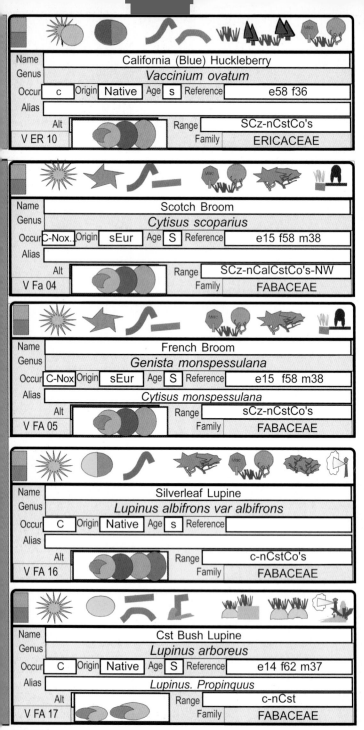

Name	California (Blue) Huckleberry
Genus	*Vaccinium ovatum*
Occur	c	Origin	Native	Age	s	Reference	e58 f36
Alias	
Alt		Range	SCz-nCstCo's
V ER 10		Family	ERICACEAE

Name	Scotch Broom
Genus	*Cytisus scoparius*
Occur	C-Nox.	Origin	sEur	Age	S	Reference	e15 f58 m38
Alias	
Alt		Range	SCz-nCalCstCo's-NW
V Fa 04		Family	FABACEAE

Name	French Broom
Genus	*Genista monspessulana*
Occur	C-Nox	Origin	sEur	Age	S	Reference	e15 f58 m38
Alias	*Cytisus monspessulana*
Alt		Range	sCz-nCstCo's
V FA 05		Family	FABACEAE

Name	Silverleaf Lupine
Genus	*Lupinus albifrons var albifrons*
Occur	C	Origin	Native	Age	s	Reference	
Alias	
Alt		Range	c-nCstCo's
V FA 16		Family	FABACEAE

Name	Cst Bush Lupine
Genus	*Lupinus arboreus*
Occur	C	Origin	Native	Age	S	Reference	e14 f62 m37
Alias	*Lupinus. Propinquus*
Alt		Range	c-nCst
V FA 17		Family	FABACEAE

W 24

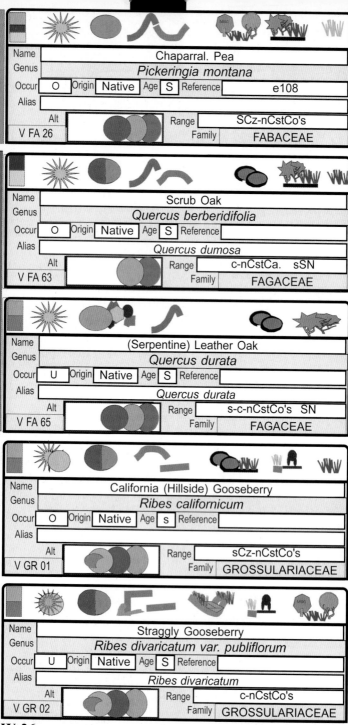

Name	Chaparral. Pea
Genus	*Pickeringia montana*
Occur	O	Origin	Native	Age	S	Reference	e108
Alias	

Alt		Range	SCz-nCstCo's
V FA 26		Family	FABACEAE

Name	Scrub Oak
Genus	*Quercus berberidifolia*
Occur	O	Origin	Native	Age	S	Reference	
Alias	*Quercus dumosa*

Alt		Range	c-nCstCa. sSN
V FA 63		Family	FAGACEAE

Name	(Serpentine) Leather Oak
Genus	*Quercus durata*
Occur	U	Origin	Native	Age	S	Reference	
Alias	*Quercus durata*

Alt		Range	s-c-nCstCo's SN
V FA 65		Family	FAGACEAE

Name	California (Hillside) Gooseberry
Genus	*Ribes californicum*
Occur	O	Origin	Native	Age	s	Reference	
Alias	

Alt		Range	sCz-nCstCo's
V GR 01		Family	GROSSULARIACEAE

Name	Straggly Gooseberry
Genus	*Ribes divaricatum var. publiflorum*
Occur	U	Origin	Native	Age	S	Reference	
Alias	*Ribes divaricatum*

Alt		Range	c-nCstCo's
V GR 02		Family	GROSSULARIACEAE

W 26

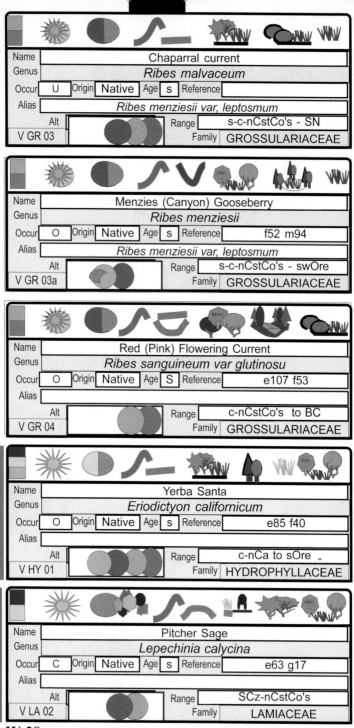

Name	Chaparral current
Genus	*Ribes malvaceum*
Occur	U Origin Native Age s Reference
Alias	*Ribes menziesii var, leptosmum*
Alt	Range s-c-nCstCo's - SN
V GR 03	Family GROSSULARIACEAE

Name	Menzies (Canyon) Gooseberry
Genus	*Ribes menziesii*
Occur	O Origin Native Age s Reference f52 m94
Alias	*Ribes menziesii var, leptosmum*
Alt	Range s-c-nCstCo's - swOre
V GR 03a	Family GROSSULARIACEAE

Name	Red (Pink) Flowering Current
Genus	*Ribes sanguineum var glutinosu*
Occur	O Origin Native Age S Reference e107 f53
Alias	
Alt	Range c-nCstCo's to BC
V GR 04	Family GROSSULARIACEAE

Name	Yerba Santa
Genus	*Eriodictyon californicum*
Occur	O Origin Native Age s Reference e85 f40
Alias	
Alt	Range c-nCa to sOre
V HY 01	Family HYDROPHYLLACEAE

Name	Pitcher Sage
Genus	*Lepechinia calycina*
Occur	C Origin Native Age s Reference e63 g17
Alias	
Alt	Range SCz-nCstCo's
V LA 02	Family LAMIACEAE

W 28

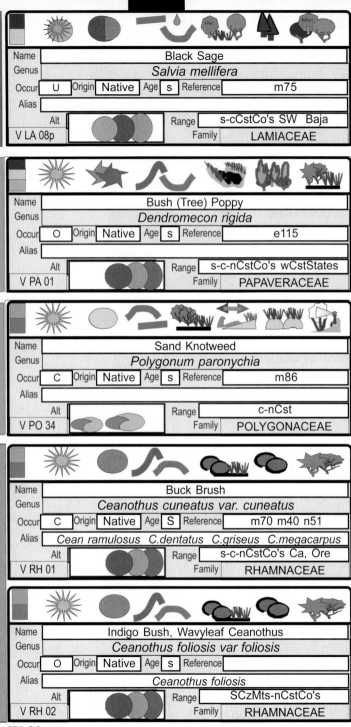

Name	Black Sage
Genus	*Salvia mellifera*
Occur	U	Origin	Native	Age	s	Reference	m75
Alias	
Alt		Range	s-cCstCo's SW Baja
V LA 08p		Family	LAMIACEAE

Name	Bush (Tree) Poppy
Genus	*Dendromecon rigida*
Occur	O	Origin	Native	Age	s	Reference	e115
Alias	
Alt		Range	s-c-nCstCo's wCstStates
V PA 01		Family	PAPAVERACEAE

Name	Sand Knotweed
Genus	*Polygonum paronychia*
Occur	C	Origin	Native	Age	s	Reference	m86
Alias	
Alt		Range	c-nCst
V PO 34		Family	POLYGONACEAE

Name	Buck Brush
Genus	*Ceanothus cuneatus var. cuneatus*
Occur	C	Origin	Native	Age	S	Reference	m70 m40 n51
Alias	*Cean ramulosus C.dentatus C.griseus C.megacarpus*
Alt		Range	s-c-nCstCo's Ca, Ore
V RH 01		Family	RHAMNACEAE

Name	Indigo Bush, Wavyleaf Ceanothus
Genus	*Ceanothus foliosis var foliosis*
Occur	O	Origin	Native	Age	s	Reference	
Alias	*Ceanothus foliosis*
Alt		Range	SCzMts-nCstCo's
V RH 02		Family	RHAMNACEAE

W 30

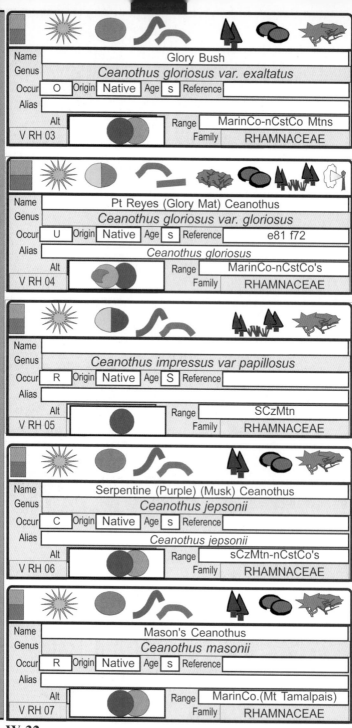

Name		Glory Bush
Genus		*Ceanothus gloriosus var. exaltatus*
Occur	O	Origin Native	Age	s	Reference	
Alias		
Alt		Range	MarinCo-nCstCo Mtns
V RH 03		Family	RHAMNACEAE

Name		Pt Reyes (Glory Mat) Ceanothus
Genus		*Ceanothus gloriosus var. gloriosus*
Occur	U	Origin Native	Age	s	Reference	e81 f72
Alias		*Ceanothus gloriosus*
Alt		Range	MarinCo-nCstCo's
V RH 04		Family	RHAMNACEAE

Name		
Genus		*Ceanothus impressus var papillosus*
Occur	R	Origin Native	Age	S	Reference	
Alias		
Alt		Range	SCzMtn
V RH 05		Family	RHAMNACEAE

Name		Serpentine (Purple) (Musk) Ceanothus
Genus		*Ceanothus jepsonii*
Occur	C	Origin Native	Age	s	Reference	
Alias		*Ceanothus jepsonii*
Alt		Range	sCzMtn-nCstCo's
V RH 06		Family	RHAMNACEAE

Name		Mason's Ceanothus
Genus		*Ceanothus masonii*
Occur	R	Origin Native	Age	s	Reference	
Alias		
Alt		Range	MarinCo.(Mt Tamalpais)
V RH 07		Family	RHAMNACEAE

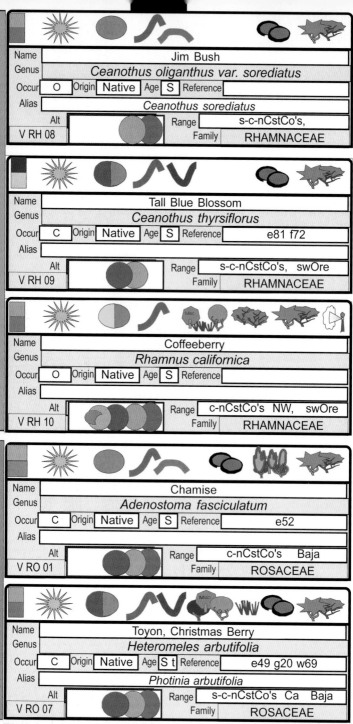

Name Jim Bush
Genus *Ceanothus oliganthus var. sorediatus*
Occur O **Origin** Native **Age** S **Reference**
Alias *Ceanothus sorediatus*
Alt **Range** s-c-nCstCo's,
V RH 08 **Family** RHAMNACEAE

Name Tall Blue Blossom
Genus *Ceanothus thyrsiflorus*
Occur C **Origin** Native **Age** S **Reference** e81 f72
Alias
Alt **Range** s-c-nCstCo's, swOre
V RH 09 **Family** RHAMNACEAE

Name Coffeeberry
Genus *Rhamnus californica*
Occur O **Origin** Native **Age** S **Reference**
Alias
Alt **Range** c-nCstCo's NW, swOre
V RH 10 **Family** RHAMNACEAE

Name Chamise
Genus *Adenostoma fasciculatum*
Occur C **Origin** Native **Age** S **Reference** e52
Alias
Alt **Range** c-nCstCo's Baja
V RO 01 **Family** ROSACEAE

Name Toyon, Christmas Berry
Genus *Heteromeles arbutifolia*
Occur C **Origin** Native **Age** S t **Reference** e49 g20 w69
Alias *Photinia arbutifolia*
Alt **Range** s-c-nCstCo's Ca Baja
V RO 07 **Family** ROSACEAE

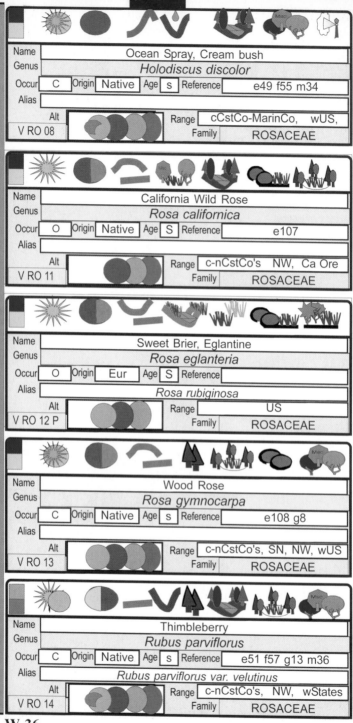

Name	Ocean Spray, Cream bush
Genus	*Holodiscus discolor*
Occur	C Origin	Native Age	s Reference	e49 f55 m34
Alias	
Alt	Range	cCstCo-MarinCo, wUS,
V RO 08	Family	ROSACEAE

Name	California Wild Rose
Genus	*Rosa californica*
Occur	O Origin	Native Age	S Reference	e107
Alias	
Alt	Range	c-nCstCo's NW, Ca Ore
V RO 11	Family	ROSACEAE

Name	Sweet Brier, Eglantine
Genus	*Rosa eglanteria*
Occur	O Origin	Eur Age	S Reference	
Alias	*Rosa rubiginosa*
Alt	Range	US
V RO 12 P	Family	ROSACEAE

Name	Wood Rose
Genus	*Rosa gymnocarpa*
Occur	C Origin	Native Age	s Reference	e108 g8
Alias	
Alt	Range	c-nCstCo's, SN, NW, wUS
V RO 13	Family	ROSACEAE

Name	Thimbleberry
Genus	*Rubus parviflorus*
Occur	C Origin	Native Age	s Reference	e51 f57 g13 m36
Alias	*Rubus parviflorus var. velutinus*
Alt	Range	c-nCstCo's, NW, wStates
V RO 14	Family	ROSACEAE

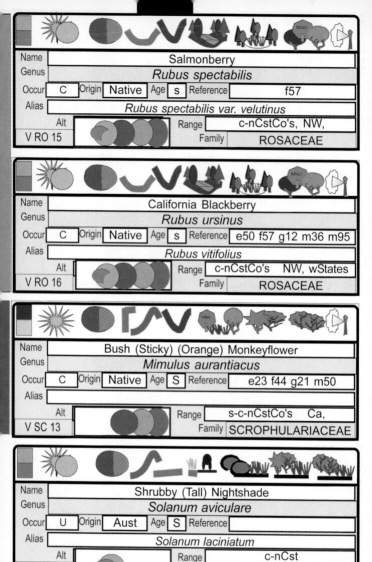

Name	Salmonberry
Genus	*Rubus spectabilis*
Occur	C	Origin	Native	Age	s	Reference	f57
Alias	*Rubus spectabilis var. velutinus*
Alt		Range	c-nCstCo's, NW,
V RO 15		Family	ROSACEAE

Name	California Blackberry
Genus	*Rubus ursinus*
Occur	C	Origin	Native	Age	s	Reference	e50 f57 g12 m36 m95
Alias	*Rubus vitifolius*
Alt		Range	c-nCstCo's NW, wStates
V RO 16		Family	ROSACEAE

Name	Bush (Sticky) (Orange) Monkeyflower
Genus	*Mimulus aurantiacus*
Occur	C	Origin	Native	Age	S	Reference	e23 f44 g21 m50
Alias	
Alt		Range	s-c-nCstCo's Ca,
V SC 13		Family	SCROPHULARIACEAE

Name	Shrubby (Tall) Nightshade
Genus	*Solanum aviculare*
Occur	U	Origin	Aust	Age	S	Reference	
Alias	*Solanum laciniatum*
Alt		Range	c-nCst
V SO 01		Family	SOLANACEAE

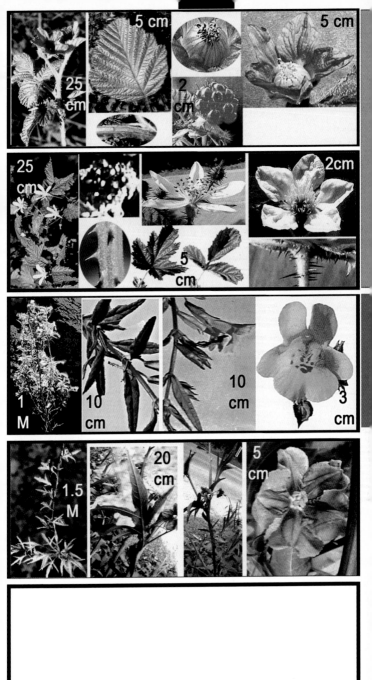

Major Dicot Families

Name	Coastal (Henderson's) Angelica
Genus	*Angelica hendersonii*
Occur	C Origin	Native Age	p Reference m99 n64
Alias	*Angellica tomentosa var hendersonii*
Alt	Range c-nCst- NW(Cst)
x AP 01	Family APIACEAE

Name	Poison Hemlock
Genus	*Conium maculatum*
Occur	C Origin	Eur Age	b Reference e55 f37 g9 m43 n64
Alias	
Alt	Range s-c-nCstCo's wUS US
x AP 02	Family APIACEAE

Name	Sweet Fennel
Genus	*Foeniculum vulgare*
Occur	LC Origin	Med Age	p Reference e19 n170
Alias	
Alt	Range Ca, US
x AP 03	Family APIACEAE

Name	Cow Parsnip
Genus	*Heracleum lanatum*
Occur	C Origin	Native Age	p Reference	e56 f73 g20 m44 n64 s28 s124
Alias	*Heracleum maximum*
Alt	Range s-c-nCstCo's, wUS eUS
x AP 04	Family APIACEAE

X 3

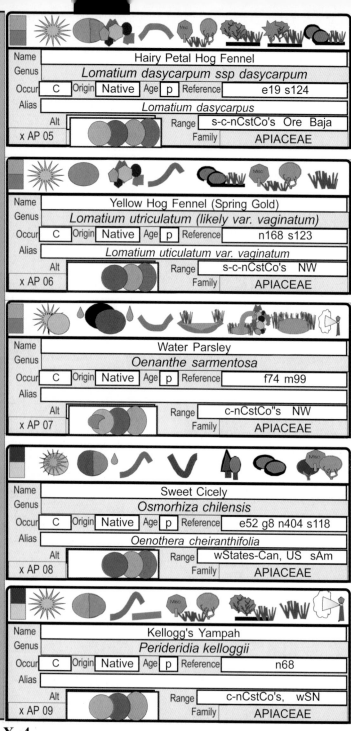

Name	Hairy Petal Hog Fennel
Genus	*Lomatium dasycarpum ssp dasycarpum*
Occur	C	Origin	Native	Age	p	Reference	e19 s124
Alias	*Lomatium dasycarpus*
Alt		Range	s-c-nCstCo's Ore Baja
x AP 05		Family	APIACEAE

Name	Yellow Hog Fennel (Spring Gold)
Genus	*Lomatium utriculatum (likely var. vaginatum)*
Occur	C	Origin	Native	Age	p	Reference	n168 s123
Alias	*Lomatium uticulatum var. vaginatum*
Alt		Range	s-c-nCstCo's NW
x AP 06		Family	APIACEAE

Name	Water Parsley
Genus	*Oenanthe sarmentosa*
Occur	C	Origin	Native	Age	p	Reference	f74 m99
Alias	
Alt		Range	c-nCstCo"s NW
x AP 07		Family	APIACEAE

Name	Sweet Cicely
Genus	*Osmorhiza chilensis*
Occur	C	Origin	Native	Age	p	Reference	e52 g8 n404 s118
Alias	*Oenothera cheiranthifolia*
Alt		Range	wStates-Can, US sAm
x AP 08		Family	APIACEAE

Name	Kellogg's Yampah
Genus	*Perideridia kelloggii*
Occur	C	Origin	Native	Age	p	Reference	n68
Alias	
Alt		Range	c-nCstCo's, wSN
x AP 09		Family	APIACEAE

X 4

X 5

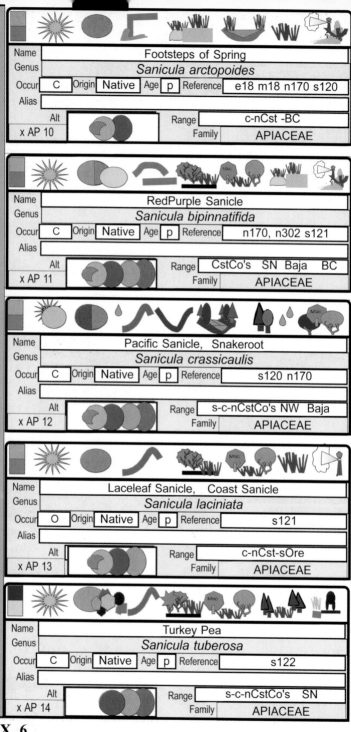

Name	Footsteps of Spring
Genus	*Sanicula arctopoides*
Occur	C Origin Native Age p Reference e18 m18 n170 s120
Alias	
Alt	Range c-nCst -BC
x AP 10	Family APIACEAE

Name	RedPurple Sanicle
Genus	*Sanicula bipinnatifida*
Occur	C Origin Native Age p Reference n170, n302 s121
Alias	
Alt	Range CstCo's SN Baja BC
x AP 11	Family APIACEAE

Name	Pacific Sanicle, Snakeroot
Genus	*Sanicula crassicaulis*
Occur	C Origin Native Age p Reference s120 n170
Alias	
Alt	Range s-c-nCstCo's NW Baja
x AP 12	Family APIACEAE

Name	Laceleaf Sanicle, Coast Sanicle
Genus	*Sanicula laciniata*
Occur	O Origin Native Age p Reference s121
Alias	
Alt	Range c-nCst-sOre
x AP 13	Family APIACEAE

Name	Turkey Pea
Genus	*Sanicula tuberosa*
Occur	C Origin Native Age p Reference s122
Alias	
Alt	Range s-c-nCstCo's SN
x AP 14	Family APIACEAE

X 6

X 7

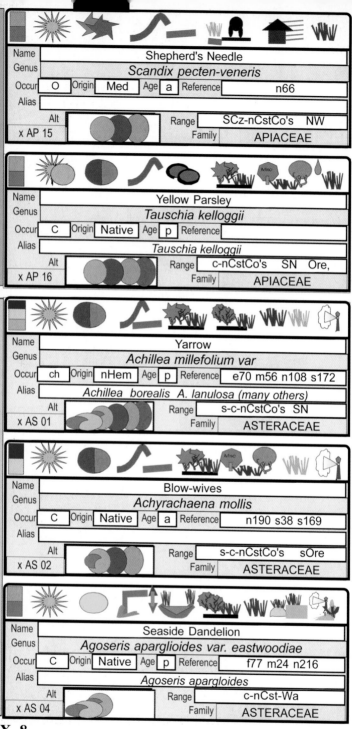

Shepherd's Needle

Name	Shepherd's Needle	
Genus	*Scandix pecten-veneris*	
Occur O	Origin Med	Age a Reference n66
Alias		
Alt		Range SCz-nCstCo's NW
x AP 15		Family APIACEAE

Yellow Parsley

Name	Yellow Parsley	
Genus	*Tauschia kelloggii*	
Occur C	Origin Native	Age p Reference
Alias	*Tauschia kelloggii*	
Alt		Range c-nCstCo's SN Ore,
x AP 16		Family APIACEAE

Yarrow

Name	Yarrow	
Genus	*Achillea millefolium var*	
Occur ch	Origin nHem	Age p Reference e70 m56 n108 s172
Alias	*Achillea borealis A. lanulosa (many others)*	
Alt		Range s-c-nCstCo's SN
x AS 01		Family ASTERACEAE

Blow-wives

Name	Blow-wives	
Genus	*Achyrachaena mollis*	
Occur C	Origin Native	Age a Reference n190 s38 s169
Alias		
Alt		Range s-c-nCstCo's sOre
x AS 02		Family ASTERACEAE

Seaside Dandelion

Name	Seaside Dandelion	
Genus	*Agoseris apargioides var. eastwoodiae*	
Occur C	Origin Native	Age p Reference f77 m24 n216
Alias	*Agoseris apargioides*	
Alt		Range c-nCst-Wa
x AS 04		Family ASTERACEAE

X 8

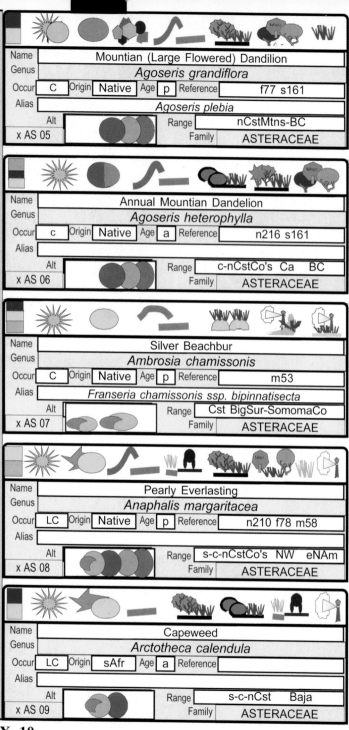

Name	Mountian (Large Flowered) Dandilion
Genus	*Agoseris grandiflora*
Occur	C	Origin	Native	Age	p	Reference	f77 s161
Alias	*Agoseris plebia*
Alt		Range	nCstMtns-BC
x AS 05		Family	ASTERACEAE

Name	Annual Mountian Dandelion
Genus	*Agoseris heterophylla*
Occur	c	Origin	Native	Age	a	Reference	n216 s161
Alias	
Alt		Range	c-nCstCo's Ca BC
x AS 06		Family	ASTERACEAE

Name	Silver Beachbur
Genus	*Ambrosia chamissonis*
Occur	C	Origin	Native	Age	p	Reference	m53
Alias	*Franseria chamissonis ssp. bipinnatisecta*
Alt		Range	Cst BigSur-SomomaCo
x AS 07		Family	ASTERACEAE

Name	Pearly Everlasting
Genus	*Anaphalis margaritacea*
Occur	LC	Origin	Native	Age	p	Reference	n210 f78 m58
Alias	
Alt		Range	s-c-nCstCo's NW eNAm
x AS 08		Family	ASTERACEAE

Name	Capeweed
Genus	*Arctotheca calendula*
Occur	LC	Origin	sAfr	Age	a	Reference	
Alias	
Alt		Range	s-c-nCst Baja
x AS 09		Family	ASTERACEAE

X 10

X 11

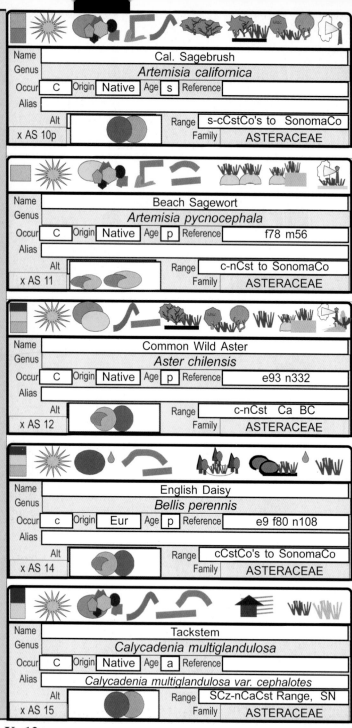

Name	Cal. Sagebrush
Genus	*Artemisia californica*
Occur	C	Origin	Native	Age	s	Reference	
Alias	
Alt		Range	s-cCstCo's to SonomaCo
x AS 10p		Family	ASTERACEAE

Name	Beach Sagewort
Genus	*Artemisia pycnocephala*
Occur	C	Origin	Native	Age	p	Reference	f78 m56
Alias	
Alt		Range	c-nCst to SonomaCo
x AS 11		Family	ASTERACEAE

Name	Common Wild Aster
Genus	*Aster chilensis*
Occur	C	Origin	Native	Age	p	Reference	e93 n332
Alias	
Alt		Range	c-nCst Ca BC
x AS 12		Family	ASTERACEAE

Name	English Daisy
Genus	*Bellis perennis*
Occur	c	Origin	Eur	Age	p	Reference	e9 f80 n108
Alias	
Alt		Range	cCstCo's to SonomaCo
x AS 14		Family	ASTERACEAE

Name	Tackstem
Genus	*Calycadenia multiglandulosa*
Occur	C	Origin	Native	Age	a	Reference	
Alias	*Calycadenia multiglandulosa var. cephalotes*
Alt		Range	SCz-nCaCst Range, SN
x AS 15		Family	ASTERACEAE

X 12

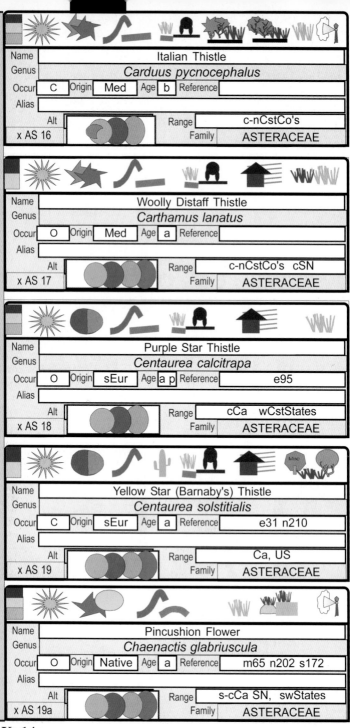

Name	Italian Thistle	
Genus	*Carduus pycnocephalus*	
Occur	C	Origin	Med	Age	b	Reference	
Alias		
Alt		Range	c-nCstCo's
x AS 16		Family	ASTERACEAE

Name	Woolly Distaff Thistle	
Genus	*Carthamus lanatus*	
Occur	O	Origin	Med	Age	a	Reference	
Alias		
Alt		Range	c-nCstCo's cSN
x AS 17		Family	ASTERACEAE

Name	Purple Star Thistle	
Genus	*Centaurea calcitrapa*	
Occur	O	Origin	sEur	Age	a p	Reference	e95
Alias		
Alt		Range	cCa wCstStates
x AS 18		Family	ASTERACEAE

Name	Yellow Star (Barnaby's) Thistle	
Genus	*Centaurea solstitialis*	
Occur	C	Origin	sEur	Age	a	Reference	e31 n210
Alias		
Alt		Range	Ca, US
x AS 19		Family	ASTERACEAE

Name	Pincushion Flower	
Genus	*Chaenactis glabriuscula*	
Occur	O	Origin	Native	Age	a	Reference	m65 n202 s172
Alias		
Alt		Range	s-cCa SN, swStates
x AS 19a		Family	ASTERACEAE

X 14

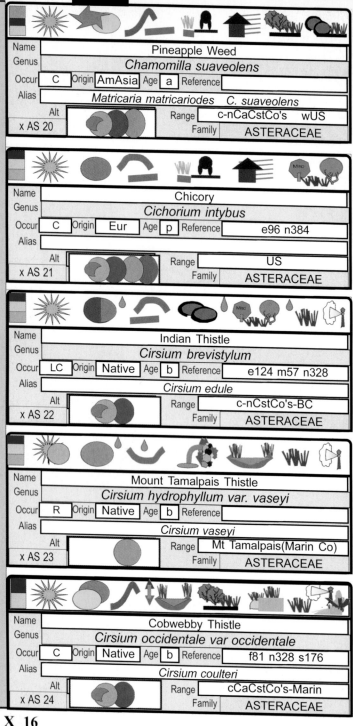

Name	Pineapple Weed
Genus	*Chamomilla suaveolens*

Occur	C	Origin	AmAsia	Age	a	Reference	

Alias	*Matricaria matricariodes* *C. suaveolens*

Alt	Range	c-nCaCstCo's wUS
x AS 20	Family	ASTERACEAE

Name	Chicory
Genus	*Cichorium intybus*

Occur	C	Origin	Eur	Age	p	Reference	e96 n384

Alias	

Alt	Range	US
x AS 21	Family	ASTERACEAE

Name	Indian Thistle
Genus	*Cirsium brevistylum*

Occur	LC	Origin	Native	Age	b	Reference	e124 m57 n328

Alias	*Cirsium edule*

Alt	Range	c-nCstCo's-BC
x AS 22	Family	ASTERACEAE

Name	Mount Tamalpais Thistle
Genus	*Cirsium hydrophyllum var. vaseyi*

Occur	R	Origin	Native	Age	b	Reference	

Alias	*Cirsium vaseyi*

Alt	Range	Mt Tamalpais(Marin Co)
x AS 23	Family	ASTERACEAE

Name	Cobwebby Thistle
Genus	*Cirsium occidentale var occidentale*

Occur	C	Origin	Native	Age	b	Reference	f81 n328 s176

Alias	*Cirsium coulteri*

Alt	Range	cCaCstCo's-Marin
x AS 24	Family	ASTERACEAE

X 16

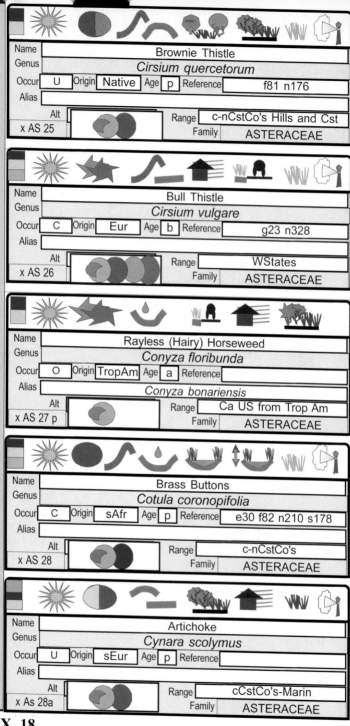

Brownie Thistle

Name	Brownie Thistle
Genus	*Cirsium quercetorum*
Occur	U	Origin	Native	Age	p	Reference	f81 n176

Alias

Alt
x AS 25
Range: c-nCstCo's Hills and Cst
Family: ASTERACEAE

Bull Thistle

Name	Bull Thistle
Genus	*Cirsium vulgare*
Occur	C	Origin	Eur	Age	b	Reference	g23 n328

Alias

Alt
x AS 26
Range: WStates
Family: ASTERACEAE

Rayless (Hairy) Horseweed

Name	Rayless (Hairy) Horseweed
Genus	*Conyza floribunda*
Occur	O	Origin	TropAm	Age	a	Reference	

Alias: *Conyza bonariensis*

Alt
x AS 27 p
Range: Ca US from Trop Am
Family: ASTERACEAE

Brass Buttons

Name	Brass Buttons
Genus	*Cotula coronopifolia*
Occur	C	Origin	sAfr	Age	p	Reference	e30 f82 n210 s178

Alias

Alt
x AS 28
Range: c-nCstCo's
Family: ASTERACEAE

Artichoke

Name	Artichoke
Genus	*Cynara scolymus*
Occur	U	Origin	sEur	Age	p	Reference	

Alias

Alt
x As 28a
Range: cCstCo's-Marin
Family: ASTERACEAE

X 18

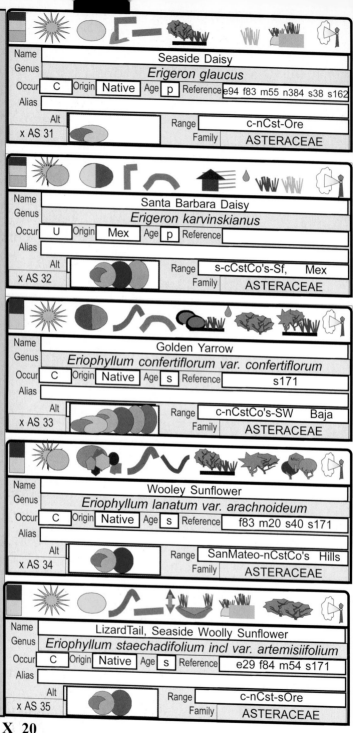

Name	Seaside Daisy
Genus	*Erigeron glaucus*
Occur	C Origin Native Age p Reference e94 f83 m55 n384 s38 s162
Alias	
Alt	Range c-nCst-Ore
x AS 31	Family ASTERACEAE

Name	Santa Barbara Daisy
Genus	*Erigeron karvinskianus*
Occur	U Origin Mex Age p Reference
Alias	
Alt	Range s-cCstCo's-Sf, Mex
x AS 32	Family ASTERACEAE

Name	Golden Yarrow
Genus	*Eriophyllum confertiflorum var. confertiflorum*
Occur	C Origin Native Age s Reference s171
Alias	
Alt	Range c-nCstCo's-SW Baja
x AS 33	Family ASTERACEAE

Name	Wooley Sunflower
Genus	*Eriophyllum lanatum var. arachnoideum*
Occur	C Origin Native Age s Reference f83 m20 s40 s171
Alias	
Alt	Range SanMateo-nCstCo's Hills
x AS 34	Family ASTERACEAE

Name	LizardTail, Seaside Woolly Sunflower
Genus	*Eriophyllum staechadifolium incl var. artemisiifolium*
Occur	C Origin Native Age s Reference e29 f84 m54 s171
Alias	
Alt	Range c-nCst-sOre
x AS 35	Family ASTERACEAE

X 20

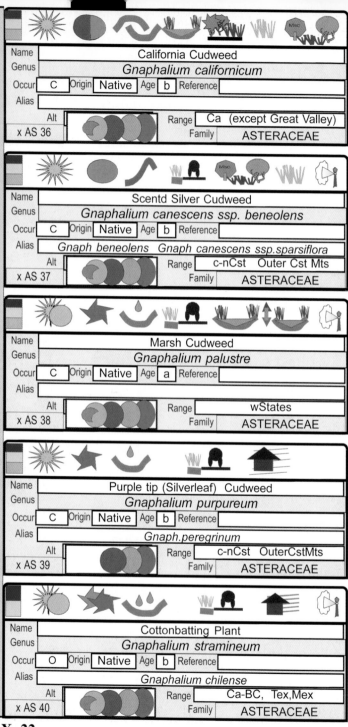

Name	California Cudweed
Genus	*Gnaphalium californicum*
Occur	C Origin Native Age b Reference
Alias	
Alt	Range Ca (except Great Valley)
x AS 36	Family ASTERACEAE

Name	Scentd Silver Cudweed
Genus	*Gnaphalium canescens ssp. beneolens*
Occur	C Origin Native Age b Reference
Alias	*Gnaph beneolens Gnaph canescens ssp.sparsiflora*
Alt	Range c-nCst Outer Cst Mts
x AS 37	Family ASTERACEAE

Name	Marsh Cudweed
Genus	*Gnaphalium palustre*
Occur	C Origin Native Age a Reference
Alias	
Alt	Range wStates
x AS 38	Family ASTERACEAE

Name	Purple tip (Silverleaf) Cudweed
Genus	*Gnaphalium purpureum*
Occur	C Origin Native Age b Reference
Alias	*Gnaph.peregrinum*
Alt	Range c-nCst OuterCstMts
x AS 39	Family ASTERACEAE

Name	Cottonbatting Plant
Genus	*Gnaphalium stramineum*
Occur	O Origin Native Age b Reference
Alias	*Gnaphalium chilense*
Alt	Range Ca-BC, Tex,Mex
x AS 40	Family ASTERACEAE

X 23

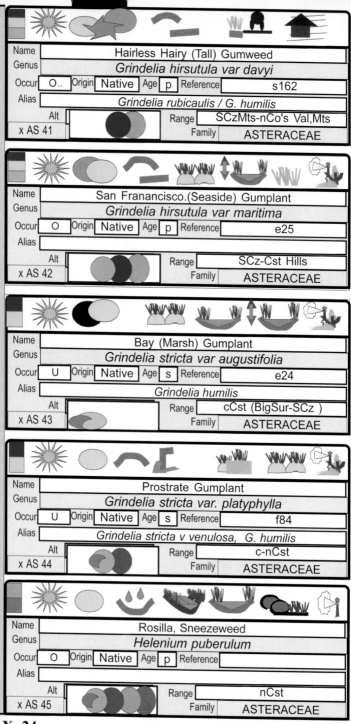

Name: Hairless Hairy (Tall) Gumweed
Genus: *Grindelia hirsutula var davyi*
Occur: O..   **Origin:** Native   **Age:** p   **Reference:** s162
Alias: *Grindelia rubicaulis / G. humilis*
Alt: **Range:** SCzMts-nCo's Val,Mts
x AS 41   **Family:** ASTERACEAE

Name: San Franancisco.(Seaside) Gumplant
Genus: *Grindelia hirsutula var maritima*
Occur: O   **Origin:** Native   **Age:** p   **Reference:** e25
Alias:
Alt: **Range:** SCz-Cst Hills
x AS 42   **Family:** ASTERACEAE

Name: Bay (Marsh) Gumplant
Genus: *Grindelia stricta var augustifolia*
Occur: U   **Origin:** Native   **Age:** s   **Reference:** e24
Alias: *Grindelia humilis*
Alt: **Range:** cCst (BigSur-SCz)
x AS 43   **Family:** ASTERACEAE

Name: Prostrate Gumplant
Genus: *Grindelia stricta var. platyphylla*
Occur: U   **Origin:** Native   **Age:** s   **Reference:** f84
Alias: *Grindelia stricta v venulosa, G. humilis*
Alt: **Range:** c-nCst
x AS 44   **Family:** ASTERACEAE

Name: Rosilla, Sneezeweed
Genus: *Helenium puberulum*
Occur: O   **Origin:** Native   **Age:** p   **Reference:**
Alias:
Alt: **Range:** nCst
x AS 45   **Family:** ASTERACEAE

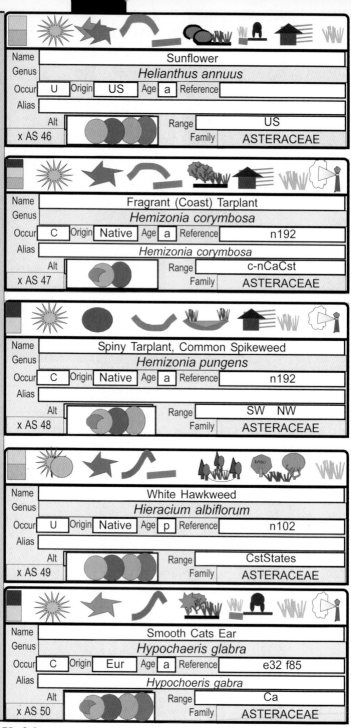

Name	Sunflower
Genus	*Helianthus annuus*
Occur	U Origin US Age a Reference
Alias	
Alt	Range US
x AS 46	Family ASTERACEAE

Name	Fragrant (Coast) Tarplant
Genus	*Hemizonia corymbosa*
Occur	C Origin Native Age a Reference n192
Alias	*Hemizonia corymbosa*
Alt	Range c-nCaCst
x AS 47	Family ASTERACEAE

Name	Spiny Tarplant, Common Spikeweed
Genus	*Hemizonia pungens*
Occur	C Origin Native Age a Reference n192
Alias	
Alt	Range SW NW
x AS 48	Family ASTERACEAE

Name	White Hawkweed
Genus	*Hieracium albiflorum*
Occur	U Origin Native Age p Reference n102
Alias	
Alt	Range CstStates
x AS 49	Family ASTERACEAE

Name	Smooth Cats Ear
Genus	*Hypochaeris glabra*
Occur	C Origin Eur Age a Reference e32 f85
Alias	*Hypochoeris gabra*
Alt	Range Ca
x AS 50	Family ASTERACEAE

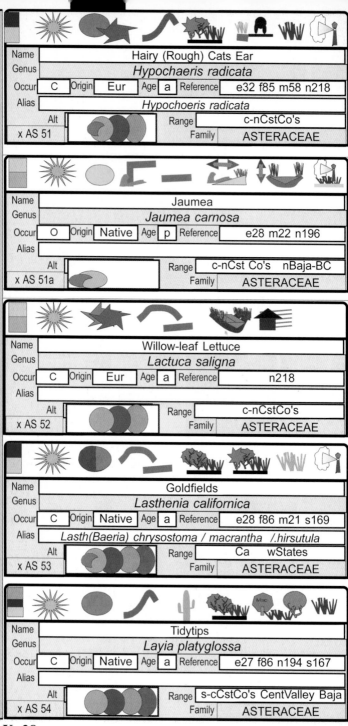

Name Hairy (Rough) Cats Ear
Genus *Hypochaeris radicata*
Occur C **Origin** Eur **Age** a **Reference** e32 f85 m58 n218
Alias *Hypochoeris radicata*
Alt
x AS 51 **Range** c-nCstCo's
Family ASTERACEAE

Name Jaumea
Genus *Jaumea carnosa*
Occur O **Origin** Native **Age** p **Reference** e28 m22 n196
Alias
Alt
x AS 51a **Range** c-nCst Co's nBaja-BC
Family ASTERACEAE

Name Willow-leaf Lettuce
Genus *Lactuca saligna*
Occur C **Origin** Eur **Age** a **Reference** n218
Alias
Alt
x AS 52 **Range** c-nCstCo's
Family ASTERACEAE

Name Goldfields
Genus *Lasthenia californica*
Occur C **Origin** Native **Age** a **Reference** e28 f86 m21 s169
Alias *Lasth(Baeria) chrysostoma / macrantha /.hirsutula*
Alt
x AS 53 **Range** Ca wStates
Family ASTERACEAE

Name Tidytips
Genus *Layia platyglossa*
Occur C **Origin** Native **Age** a **Reference** e27 f86 n194 s167
Alias
Alt
x AS 54 **Range** s-cCstCo's CentValley Baja
Family ASTERACEAE

X 28

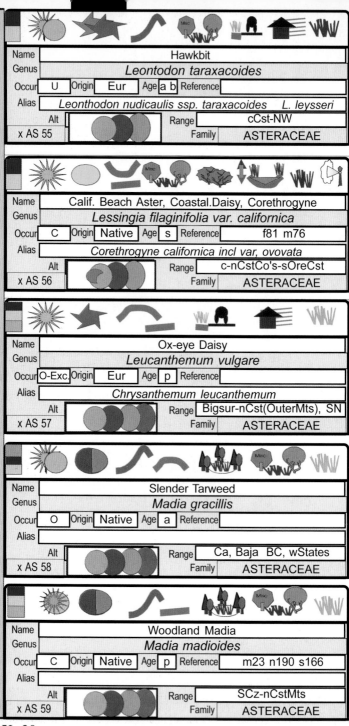

Name	Hawkbit
Genus	*Leontodon taraxacoides*
Occur	U Origin Eur Age a b Reference
Alias	*Leonthodon nudicaulis ssp. taraxacoides* *L. leysseri*
Alt	Range cCst-NW
x AS 55	Family ASTERACEAE

Name	Calif. Beach Aster, Coastal.Daisy, Corethrogyne
Genus	*Lessingia filaginifolia var. californica*
Occur	C Origin Native Age s Reference f81 m76
Alias	*Corethrogyne californica incl var, ovovata*
Alt	Range c-nCstCo's-sOreCst
x AS 56	Family ASTERACEAE

Name	Ox-eye Daisy
Genus	*Leucanthemum vulgare*
Occur	O-Exc. Origin Eur Age p Reference
Alias	*Chrysanthemum leucanthemum*
Alt	Range Bigsur-nCst(OuterMts), SN
x AS 57	Family ASTERACEAE

Name	Slender Tarweed
Genus	*Madia gracillis*
Occur	O Origin Native Age a Reference
Alias	
Alt	Range Ca, Baja BC, wStates
x AS 58	Family ASTERACEAE

Name	Woodland Madia
Genus	*Madia madioides*
Occur	C Origin Native Age p Reference m23 n190 s166
Alias	
Alt	Range SCz-nCstMts
x AS 59	Family ASTERACEAE

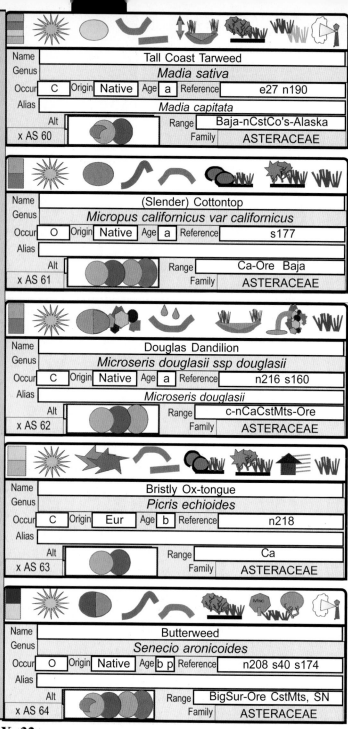

Name	Tall Coast Tarweed
Genus	*Madia sativa*
Occur	C — Origin: Native — Age: a — Reference: e27 n190
Alias	*Madia capitata*
Alt	Range: Baja-nCstCo's-Alaska
x AS 60	Family: ASTERACEAE

Name	(Slender) Cottontop
Genus	*Micropus californicus var californicus*
Occur	O — Origin: Native — Age: a — Reference: s177
Alias	
Alt	Range: Ca-Ore Baja
x AS 61	Family: ASTERACEAE

Name	Douglas Dandilion
Genus	*Microseris douglasii ssp douglasii*
Occur	C — Origin: Native — Age: a — Reference: n216 s160
Alias	*Microseris douglasii*
Alt	Range: c-nCaCstMts-Ore
x AS 62	Family: ASTERACEAE

Name	Bristly Ox-tongue
Genus	*Picris echioides*
Occur	C — Origin: Eur — Age: b — Reference: n218
Alias	
Alt	Range: Ca
x AS 63	Family: ASTERACEAE

Name	Butterweed
Genus	*Senecio aronicoides*
Occur	O — Origin: Native — Age: b p — Reference: n208 s40 s174
Alias	
Alt	Range: BigSur-Ore CstMts, SN
x AS 64	Family: ASTERACEAE

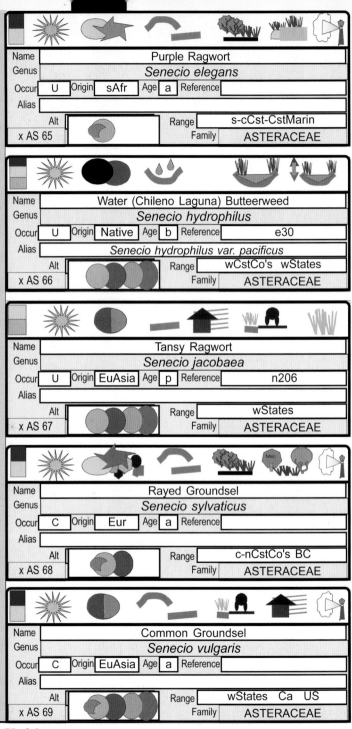

Name	Purple Ragwort
Genus	*Senecio elegans*
Occur U **Origin** sAfr **Age** a **Reference**	
Alias	
Alt	**Range** s-cCst-CstMarin
x AS 65	**Family** ASTERACEAE

Name	Water (Chileno Laguna) Butteerweed
Genus	*Senecio hydrophilus*
Occur U **Origin** Native **Age** b **Reference** e30	
Alias	*Senecio hydrophilus var. pacificus*
Alt	**Range** wCstCo's wStates
x AS 66	**Family** ASTERACEAE

Name	Tansy Ragwort
Genus	*Senecio jacobaea*
Occur U **Origin** EuAsia **Age** p **Reference** n206	
Alias	
Alt	**Range** wStates
x AS 67	**Family** ASTERACEAE

Name	Rayed Groundsel
Genus	*Senecio sylvaticus*
Occur C **Origin** Eur **Age** a **Reference**	
Alias	
Alt	**Range** c-nCstCo's BC
x AS 68	**Family** ASTERACEAE

Name	Common Groundsel
Genus	*Senecio vulgaris*
Occur C **Origin** EuAsia **Age** a **Reference**	
Alias	
Alt	**Range** wStates Ca US
x AS 69	**Family** ASTERACEAE

X 34

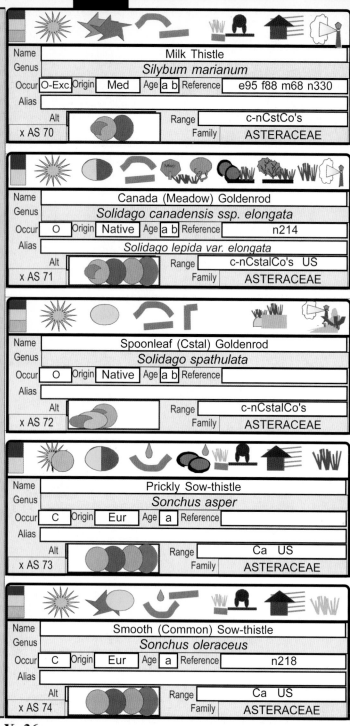

Name	Milk Thistle
Genus	*Silybum marianum*
Occur	O-Exc.	Origin	Med	Age	a b	Reference	e95 f88 m68 n330
Alias	
Alt		Range	c-nCstCo's
x AS 70		Family	ASTERACEAE

Name	Canada (Meadow) Goldenrod
Genus	*Solidago canadensis ssp. elongata*
Occur	O	Origin	Native	Age	a b	Reference	n214
Alias	*Solidago lepida var. elongata*
Alt		Range	c-nCstalCo's US
x AS 71		Family	ASTERACEAE

Name	Spoonleaf (Cstal) Goldenrod
Genus	*Solidago spathulata*
Occur	O	Origin	Native	Age	a b	Reference	
Alias	
Alt		Range	c-nCstalCo's
x AS 72		Family	ASTERACEAE

Name	Prickly Sow-thistle
Genus	*Sonchus asper*
Occur	C	Origin	Eur	Age	a	Reference	
Alias	
Alt		Range	Ca US
x AS 73		Family	ASTERACEAE

Name	Smooth (Common) Sow-thistle
Genus	*Sonchus oleraceus*
Occur	C	Origin	Eur	Age	a	Reference	n218
Alias	
Alt		Range	Ca US
x AS 74		Family	ASTERACEAE

X 36

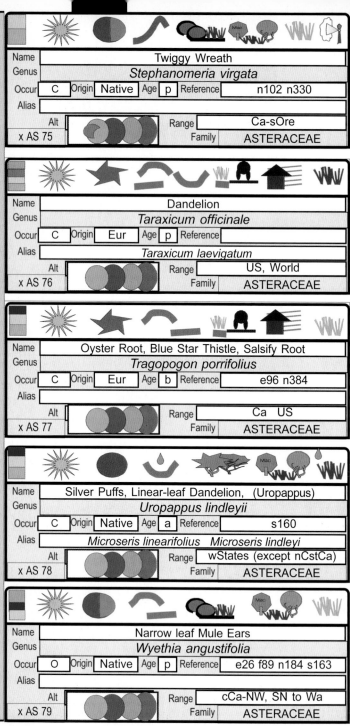

Name	Twiggy Wreath
Genus	*Stephanomeria virgata*
Occur C **Origin** Native **Age** p **Reference**	n102 n330
Alias	
Alt **Range**	Ca-sOre
x AS 75 **Family**	ASTERACEAE

Name	Dandelion
Genus	*Taraxicum officinale*
Occur C **Origin** Eur **Age** p **Reference**	
Alias	*Taraxicum laevigatum*
Alt **Range**	US, World
x AS 76 **Family**	ASTERACEAE

Name	Oyster Root, Blue Star Thistle, Salsify Root
Genus	*Tragopogon porrifolius*
Occur C **Origin** Eur **Age** b **Reference**	e96 n384
Alias	
Alt **Range**	Ca US
x AS 77 **Family**	ASTERACEAE

Name	Silver Puffs, Linear-leaf Dandelion, (Uropappus)
Genus	*Uropappus lindleyii*
Occur C **Origin** Native **Age** a **Reference**	s160
Alias	*Microseris linearifolius Microseris lindleyi*
Alt **Range**	wStates (except nCstCa)
x AS 78 **Family**	ASTERACEAE

Name	Narrow leaf Mule Ears
Genus	*Wyethia angustifolia*
Occur O **Origin** Native **Age** p **Reference**	e26 f89 n184 s163
Alias	
Alt **Range**	cCa-NW, SN to Wa
x AS 79 **Family**	ASTERACEAE

X 38

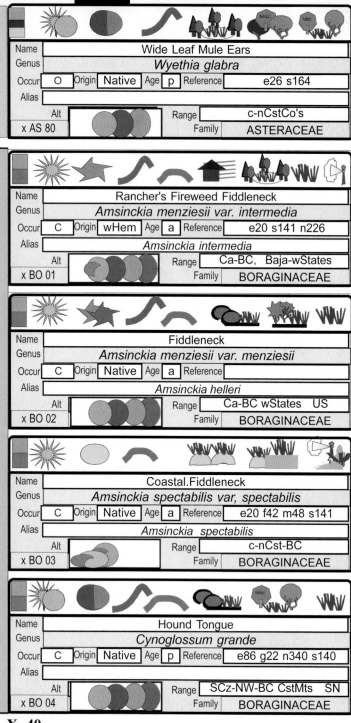

Name	Wide Leaf Mule Ears
Genus	*Wyethia glabra*
Occur O	**Origin** Native **Age** p **Reference** e26 s164
Alias	
Alt	**Range** c-nCstCo's
x AS 80	**Family** ASTERACEAE

Name	Rancher's Fireweed Fiddleneck
Genus	*Amsinckia menziesii var. intermedia*
Occur C	**Origin** wHem **Age** a **Reference** e20 s141 n226
Alias	*Amsinckia intermedia*
Alt	**Range** Ca-BC, Baja-wStates
x BO 01	**Family** BORAGINACEAE

Name	Fiddleneck
Genus	*Amsinckia menziesii var. menziesii*
Occur C	**Origin** Native **Age** a **Reference**
Alias	*Amsinckia helleri*
Alt	**Range** Ca-BC wStates US
x BO 02	**Family** BORAGINACEAE

Name	Coastal.Fiddleneck
Genus	*Amsinckia spectabilis var, spectabilis*
Occur C	**Origin** Native **Age** a **Reference** e20 f42 m48 s141
Alias	*Amsinckia spectabilis*
Alt	**Range** c-nCst-BC
x BO 03	**Family** BORAGINACEAE

Name	Hound Tongue
Genus	*Cynoglossum grande*
Occur C	**Origin** Native **Age** p **Reference** e86 g22 n340 s140
Alias	
Alt	**Range** SCz-NW-BC CstMts SN
x BO 04	**Family** BORAGINACEAE

X 40

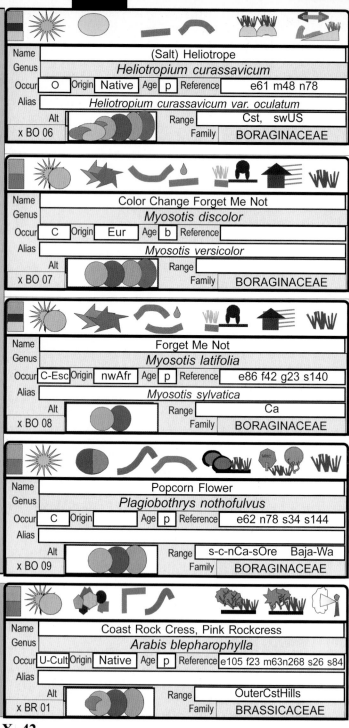

Name	(Salt) Heliotrope
Genus	*Heliotropium curassavicum*
Occur	O Origin Native Age p Reference e61 m48 n78
Alias	*Heliotropium curassavicum var. oculatum*
Alt	Range Cst, swUS
x BO 06	Family BORAGINACEAE

Name	Color Change Forget Me Not
Genus	*Myosotis discolor*
Occur	C Origin Eur Age b Reference
Alias	*Myosotis versicolor*
Alt	Range
x BO 07	Family BORAGINACEAE

Name	Forget Me Not
Genus	*Myosotis latifolia*
Occur	C-Esc Origin nwAfr Age p Reference e86 f42 g23 s140
Alias	*Myosotis sylvatica*
Alt	Range Ca
x BO 08	Family BORAGINACEAE

Name	Popcorn Flower
Genus	*Plagiobothrys nothofulvus*
Occur	C Origin Age p Reference e62 n78 s34 s144
Alias	
Alt	Range s-c-nCa-sOre Baja-Wa
x BO 09	Family BORAGINACEAE

Name	Coast Rock Cress, Pink Rockcress
Genus	*Arabis blepharophylla*
Occur	U-Cult Origin Native Age p Reference e105 f23 m63n268 s26 s84
Alias	
Alt	Range OuterCstHills
x BR 01	Family BRASSICACEAE

X 42

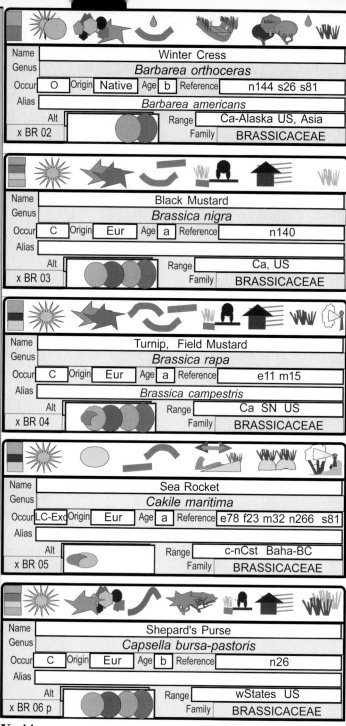

Name	Winter Cress
Genus	*Barbarea orthoceras*
Occur	O Origin Native Age b Reference n144 s26 s81
Alias	*Barbarea americans*
Alt	Range Ca-Alaska US, Asia
x BR 02	Family BRASSICACEAE

Name	Black Mustard
Genus	*Brassica nigra*
Occur	C Origin Eur Age a Reference n140
Alias	
Alt	Range Ca, US
x BR 03	Family BRASSICACEAE

Name	Turnip, Field Mustard
Genus	*Brassica rapa*
Occur	C Origin Eur Age a Reference e11 m15
Alias	*Brassica campestris*
Alt	Range Ca SN US
x BR 04	Family BRASSICACEAE

Name	Sea Rocket
Genus	*Cakile maritima*
Occur	LC-Exc Origin Eur Age a Reference e78 f23 m32 n266 s81
Alias	
Alt	Range c-nCst Baha-BC
x BR 05	Family BRASSICACEAE

Name	Shepard's Purse
Genus	*Capsella bursa-pastoris*
Occur	C Origin Eur Age b Reference n26
Alias	
Alt	Range wStates US
x BR 06 p	Family BRASSICACEAE

X 44

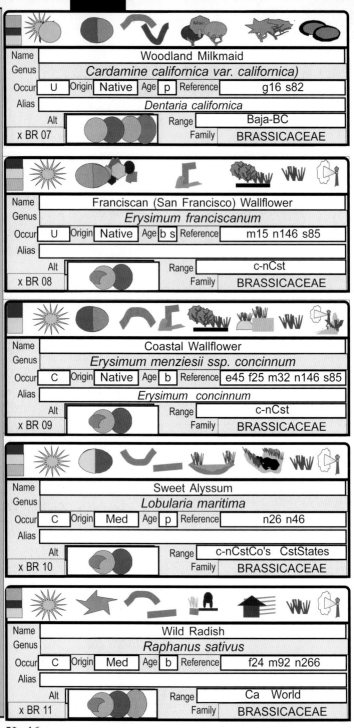

Name	Woodland Milkmaid
Genus	*Cardamine californica var. californica)*
Occur	U	Origin	Native	Age	p	Reference	g16 s82
Alias	*Dentaria californica*
Alt	Range	Baja-BC
x BR 07	Family	BRASSICACEAE

Name	Franciscan (San Francisco) Wallflower
Genus	*Erysimum franciscanum*
Occur	U	Origin	Native	Age	b s	Reference	m15 n146 s85
Alias	
Alt	Range	c-nCst
x BR 08	Family	BRASSICACEAE

Name	Coastal Wallflower
Genus	*Erysimum menziesii ssp. concinnum*
Occur	C	Origin	Native	Age	b	Reference	e45 f25 m32 n146 s85
Alias	*Erysimum concinnum*
Alt	Range	c-nCst
x BR 09	Family	BRASSICACEAE

Name	Sweet Alyssum
Genus	*Lobularia maritima*
Occur	C	Origin	Med	Age	p	Reference	n26 n46
Alias	
Alt	Range	c-nCstCo's CstStates
x BR 10	Family	BRASSICACEAE

Name	Wild Radish
Genus	*Raphanus sativus*
Occur	C	Origin	Med	Age	b	Reference	f24 m92 n266
Alias	
Alt	Range	Ca World
x BR 11	Family	BRASSICACEAE

X 46

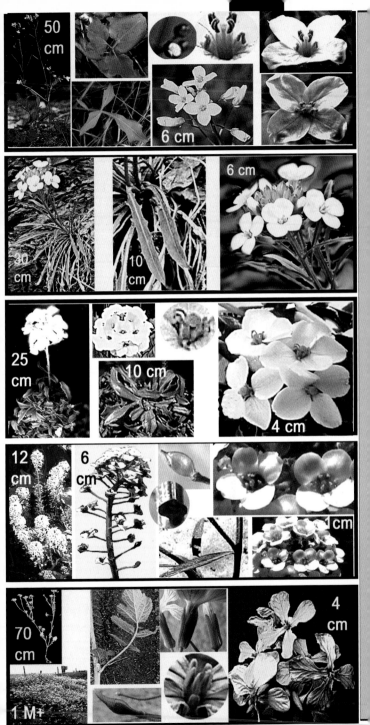

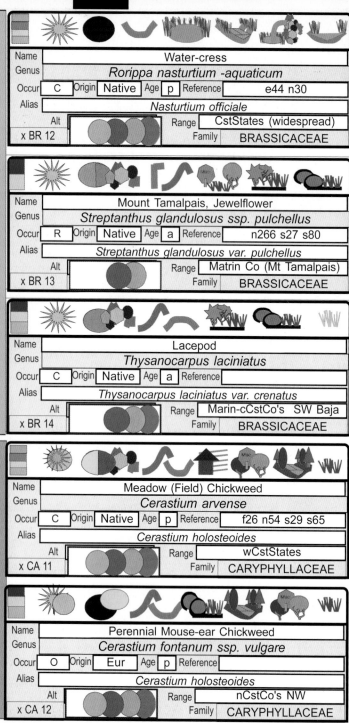

Name	Water-cress
Genus	*Rorippa nasturtium -aquaticum*
Occur	C	Origin	Native	Age	p	Reference	e44 n30
Alias	*Nasturtium officiale*
Alt		Range	CstStates (widespread)
x BR 12		Family	BRASSICACEAE

Name	Mount Tamalpais, Jewelflower
Genus	*Streptanthus glandulosus ssp. pulchellus*
Occur	R	Origin	Native	Age	a	Reference	n266 s27 s80
Alias	*Streptanthus glandulosus var. pulchellus*
Alt		Range	Matrin Co (Mt Tamalpais)
x BR 13		Family	BRASSICACEAE

Name	Lacepod
Genus	*Thysanocarpus laciniatus*
Occur	C	Origin	Native	Age	a	Reference	
Alias	*Thysanocarpus laciniatus var. crenatus*
Alt		Range	Marin-cCstCo's SW Baja
x BR 14		Family	BRASSICACEAE

Name	Meadow (Field) Chickweed
Genus	*Cerastium arvense*
Occur	C	Origin	Native	Age	p	Reference	f26 n54 s29 s65
Alias	*Cerastium holosteoides*
Alt		Range	wCstStates
x CA 11		Family	CARYPHYLLACEAE

Name	Perennial Mouse-ear Chickweed
Genus	*Cerastium fontanum ssp. vulgare*
Occur	O	Origin	Eur	Age	p	Reference	
Alias	*Cerastium holosteoides*
Alt		Range	nCstCo's NW
x CA 12		Family	CARYPHYLLACEAE

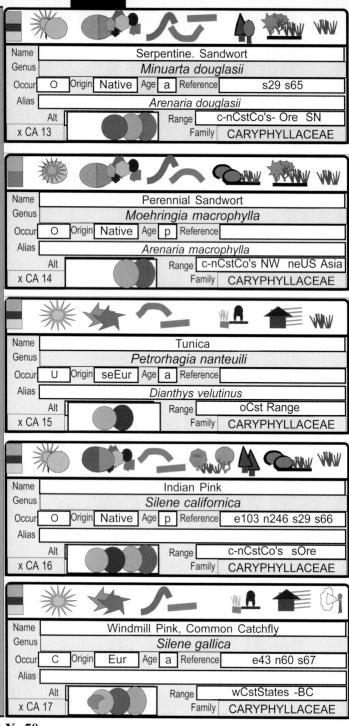

Name	Serpentine. Sandwort
Genus	*Minuarta douglasii*
Occur	O	Origin	Native	Age	a	Reference	s29 s65
Alias	*Arenaria douglasii*
Alt		Range	c-nCstCo's- Ore SN
x CA 13		Family	CARYPHYLLACEAE

Name	Perennial Sandwort
Genus	*Moehringia macrophylla*
Occur	O	Origin	Native	Age	p	Reference	
Alias	*Arenaria macrophylla*
Alt		Range	c-nCstCo's NW neUS Asia
x CA 14		Family	CARYPHYLLACEAE

Name	Tunica
Genus	*Petrorhagia nanteuili*
Occur	U	Origin	seEur	Age	a	Reference	
Alias	*Dianthys velutinus*
Alt		Range	oCst Range
x CA 15		Family	CARYPHYLLACEAE

Name	Indian Pink
Genus	*Silene californica*
Occur	O	Origin	Native	Age	p	Reference	e103 n246 s29 s66
Alias	
Alt		Range	c-nCstCo's sOre
x CA 16		Family	CARYPHYLLACEAE

Name	Windmill Pink, Common Catchfly
Genus	*Silene gallica*
Occur	C	Origin	Eur	Age	a	Reference	e43 n60 s67
Alias	
Alt		Range	wCstStates -BC
x CA 17		Family	CARYPHYLLACEAE

X 50

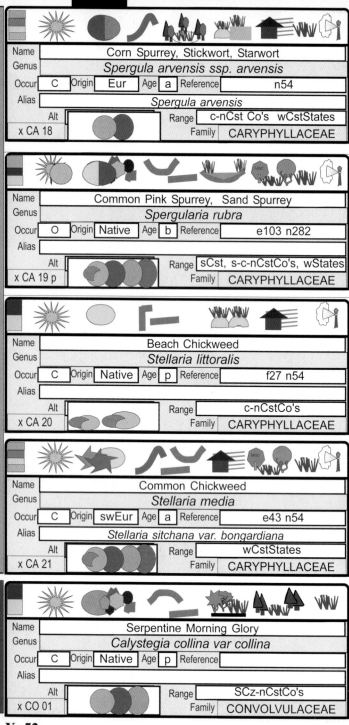

Name	Corn Spurrey, Stickwort, Starwort
Genus	*Spergula arvensis ssp. arvensis*
Occur	C — Origin Eur — Age a — Reference n54
Alias	*Spergula arvensis*
Alt	Range c-nCst Co's wCstStates
x CA 18	Family CARYPHYLLACEAE

Name	Common Pink Spurrey, Sand Spurrey
Genus	*Spergularia rubra*
Occur	O — Origin Native — Age b — Reference e103 n282
Alias	
Alt	Range sCst, s-c-nCstCo's, wStates
x CA 19 p	Family CARYPHYLLACEAE

Name	Beach Chickweed
Genus	*Stellaria littoralis*
Occur	C — Origin Native — Age p — Reference f27 n54
Alias	
Alt	Range c-nCstCo's
x CA 20	Family CARYPHYLLACEAE

Name	Common Chickweed
Genus	*Stellaria media*
Occur	C — Origin swEur — Age a — Reference e43 n54
Alias	*Stellaria sitchana var. bongardiana*
Alt	Range wCstStates
x CA 21	Family CARYPHYLLACEAE

Name	Serpentine Morning Glory
Genus	*Calystegia collina var collina*
Occur	C — Origin Native — Age p — Reference
Alias	
Alt	Range SCz-nCstCo's
x CO 01	Family CONVOLVULACEAE

X 52

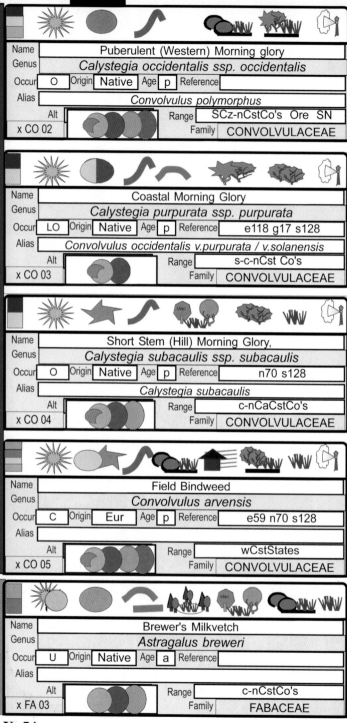

Name Puberulent (Western) Morning glory
Genus *Calystegia occidentalis ssp. occidentalis*
Occur O **Origin** Native **Age** p **Reference**
Alias *Convolvulus polymorphus*
Alt
x CO 02
Range SCz-nCstCo's Ore SN
Family CONVOLVULACEAE

Name Coastal Morning Glory
Genus *Calystegia purpurata ssp. purpurata*
Occur LO **Origin** Native **Age** p **Reference** e118 g17 s128
Alias *Convolvulus occidentalis v.purpurata / v.solanensis*
Alt
x CO 03
Range s-c-nCst Co's
Family CONVOLVULACEAE

Name Short Stem (Hill) Morning Glory,
Genus *Calystegia subacaulis ssp. subacaulis*
Occur O **Origin** Native **Age** p **Reference** n70 s128
Alias *Calystegia subacaulis*
Alt
x CO 04
Range c-nCaCstCo's
Family CONVOLVULACEAE

Name Field Bindweed
Genus *Convolvulus arvensis*
Occur C **Origin** Eur **Age** p **Reference** e59 n70 s128
Alias
Alt
x CO 05
Range wCstStates
Family CONVOLVULACEAE

Name Brewer's Milkvetch
Genus *Astragalus breweri*
Occur U **Origin** Native **Age** a **Reference**
Alias
Alt
x FA 03
Range c-nCstCo's
Family FABACEAE

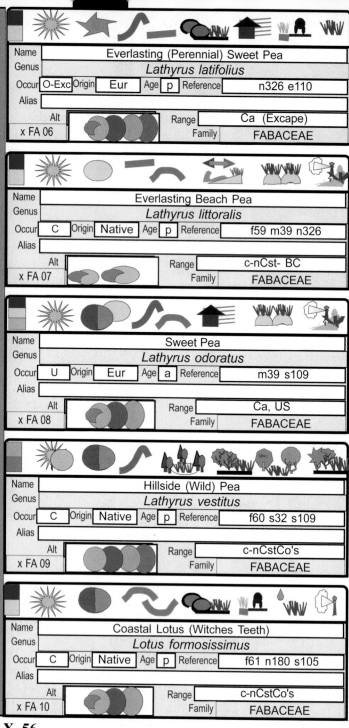

Name	Everlasting (Perennial) Sweet Pea
Genus	*Lathyrus latifolius*
Occur	O-Exc	Origin	Eur	Age	p	Reference	n326 e110
Alias	
Alt		Range	Ca (Excape)
x FA 06		Family	FABACEAE

Name	Everlasting Beach Pea
Genus	*Lathyrus littoralis*
Occur	C	Origin	Native	Age	p	Reference	f59 m39 n326
Alias	
Alt		Range	c-nCst- BC
x FA 07		Family	FABACEAE

Name	Sweet Pea
Genus	*Lathyrus odoratus*
Occur	U	Origin	Eur	Age	a	Reference	m39 s109
Alias	
Alt		Range	Ca, US
x FA 08		Family	FABACEAE

Name	Hillside (Wild) Pea
Genus	*Lathyrus vestitus*
Occur	C	Origin	Native	Age	p	Reference	f60 s32 s109
Alias	
Alt		Range	c-nCstCo's
x FA 09		Family	FABACEAE

Name	Coastal Lotus (Witches Teeth)
Genus	*Lotus formosissimus*
Occur	C	Origin	Native	Age	p	Reference	f61 n180 s105
Alias	
Alt		Range	c-nCstCo's
x FA 10		Family	FABACEAE

X 56

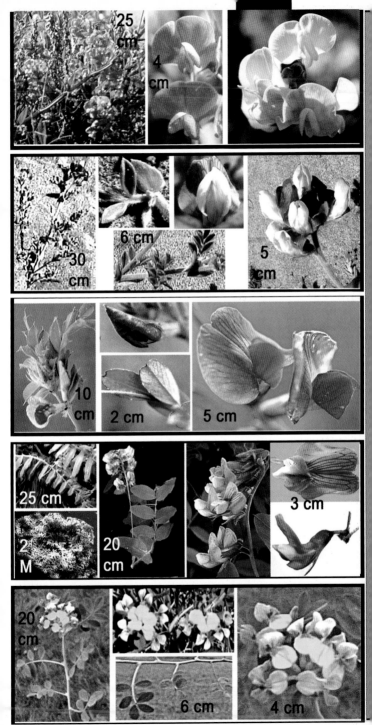

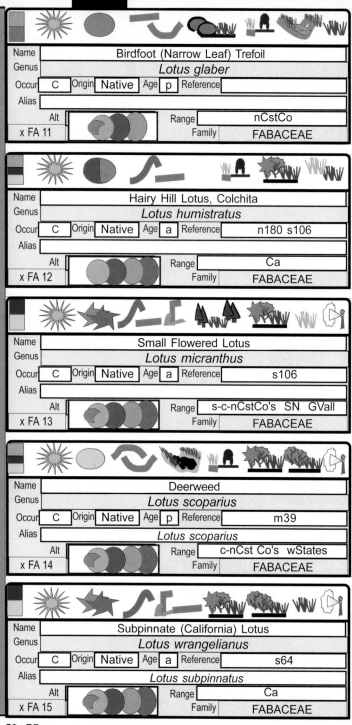

Name	Birdfoot (Narrow Leaf) Trefoil
Genus	*Lotus glaber*
Occur	C Origin Native Age p Reference
Alias	
Alt	Range nCstCo
x FA 11	Family FABACEAE

Name	Hairy Hill Lotus, Colchita
Genus	*Lotus humistratus*
Occur	C Origin Native Age a Reference n180 s106
Alias	
Alt	Range Ca
x FA 12	Family FABACEAE

Name	Small Flowered Lotus
Genus	*Lotus micranthus*
Occur	C Origin Native Age a Reference s106
Alias	
Alt	Range s-c-nCstCo's SN GVall
x FA 13	Family FABACEAE

Name	Deerweed
Genus	*Lotus scoparius*
Occur	C Origin Native Age p Reference m39
Alias	*Lotus scoparius*
Alt	Range c-nCst Co's wStates
x FA 14	Family FABACEAE

Name	Subpinnate (California) Lotus
Genus	*Lotus wrangelianus*
Occur	C Origin Native Age a Reference s64
Alias	*Lotus subpinnatus*
Alt	Range Ca
x FA 15	Family FABACEAE

X 58

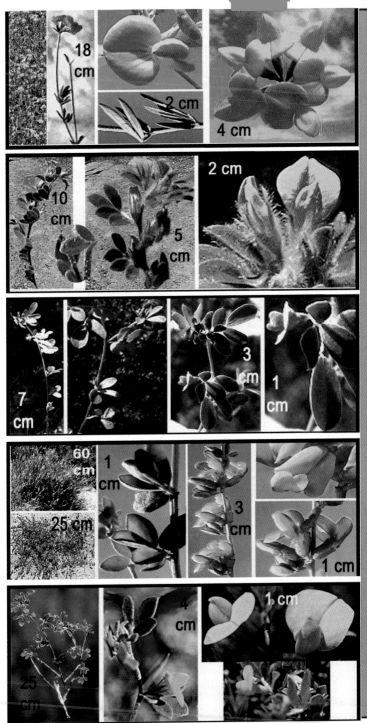

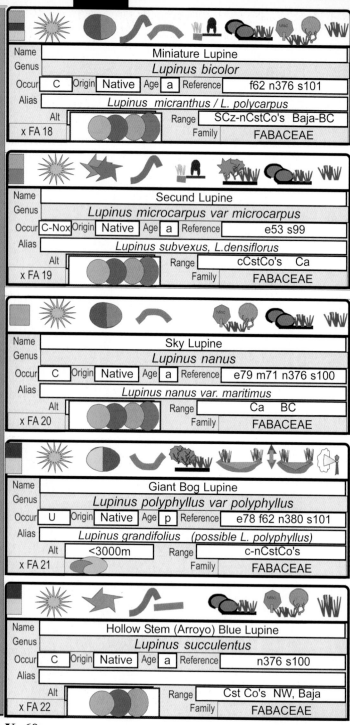

Name	Miniature Lupine
Genus	*Lupinus bicolor*
Occur	C	Origin	Native	Age	a	Reference	f62 n376 s101
Alias	*Lupinus micranthus / L. polycarpus*
Alt	Range	SCz-nCstCo's Baja-BC
x FA 18	Family	FABACEAE

Name	Secund Lupine
Genus	*Lupinus microcarpus var microcarpus*
Occur	C-Nox	Origin	Native	Age	a	Reference	e53 s99
Alias	*Lupinus subvexus, L.densiflorus*
Alt	Range	cCstCo's Ca
x FA 19	Family	FABACEAE

Name	Sky Lupine
Genus	*Lupinus nanus*
Occur	C	Origin	Native	Age	a	Reference	e79 m71 n376 s100
Alias	*Lupinus nanus var. maritimus*
Alt	Range	Ca BC
x FA 20	Family	FABACEAE

Name	Giant Bog Lupine
Genus	*Lupinus polyphyllus var polyphyllus*
Occur	U	Origin	Native	Age	p	Reference	e78 f62 n380 s101
Alias	*Lupinus grandifolius (possible L. polyphyllus)*
Alt	<3000m	Range	c-nCstCo's
x FA 21	Family	FABACEAE

Name	Hollow Stem (Arroyo) Blue Lupine
Genus	*Lupinus succulentus*
Occur	C	Origin	Native	Age	a	Reference	n376 s100
Alias	
Alt	Range	Cst Co's NW, Baja
x FA 22	Family	FABACEAE

X 60

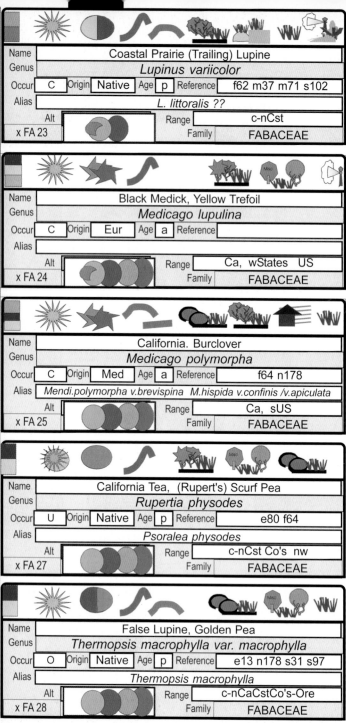

Name	Coastal Prairie (Trailing) Lupine
Genus	*Lupinus variicolor*

Occur	C	Origin	Native	Age	p	Reference	f62 m37 m71 s102

Alias	*L. littoralis ??*

Alt		Range	c-nCst
x FA 23		Family	FABACEAE

Name	Black Medick, Yellow Trefoil
Genus	*Medicago lupulina*

Occur	C	Origin	Eur	Age	a	Reference	

Alias	

Alt		Range	Ca, wStates US
x FA 24		Family	FABACEAE

Name	California. Burclover
Genus	*Medicago polymorpha*

Occur	C	Origin	Med	Age	a	Reference	f64 n178

Alias	*Mendi.polymorpha v.brevispina M.hispida v.confinis /v.apiculata*

Alt		Range	Ca, sUS
x FA 25		Family	FABACEAE

Name	California Tea, (Rupert's) Scurf Pea
Genus	*Rupertia physodes*

Occur	U	Origin	Native	Age	p	Reference	e80 f64

Alias	*Psoralea physodes*

Alt		Range	c-nCst Co's nw
x FA 27		Family	FABACEAE

Name	False Lupine, Golden Pea
Genus	*Thermopsis macrophylla var. macrophylla*

Occur	O	Origin	Native	Age	p	Reference	e13 n178 s31 s97

Alias	*Thermopsis macrophylla*

Alt		Range	c-nCaCstCo's-Ore
x FA 28		Family	FABACEAE

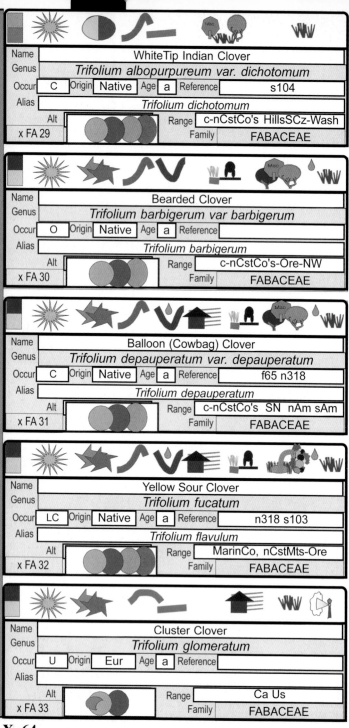

Name	WhiteTip Indian Clover
Genus	*Trifolium albopurpureum var. dichotomum*
Occur	C	Origin	Native	Age	a	Reference	s104
Alias	*Trifolium dichotomum*
Alt		Range	c-nCstCo's HillsSCz-Wash
x FA 29		Family	FABACEAE

Name	Bearded Clover
Genus	*Trifolium barbigerum var barbigerum*
Occur	O	Origin	Native	Age	a	Reference	
Alias	*Trifolium barbigerum*
Alt		Range	c-nCstCo's-Ore-NW
x FA 30		Family	FABACEAE

Name	Balloon (Cowbag) Clover
Genus	*Trifolium depauperatum var. depauperatum*
Occur	C	Origin	Native	Age	a	Reference	f65 n318
Alias	*Trifolium depauperatum*
Alt		Range	c-nCstCo's SN nAm sAm
x FA 31		Family	FABACEAE

Name	Yellow Sour Clover
Genus	*Trifolium fucatum*
Occur	LC	Origin	Native	Age	a	Reference	n318 s103
Alias	*Trifolium flavulum*
Alt		Range	MarinCo, nCstMts-Ore
x FA 32		Family	FABACEAE

Name	Cluster Clover
Genus	*Trifolium glomeratum*
Occur	U	Origin	Eur	Age	a	Reference	
Alias	
Alt		Range	Ca Us
x FA 33		Family	FABACEAE

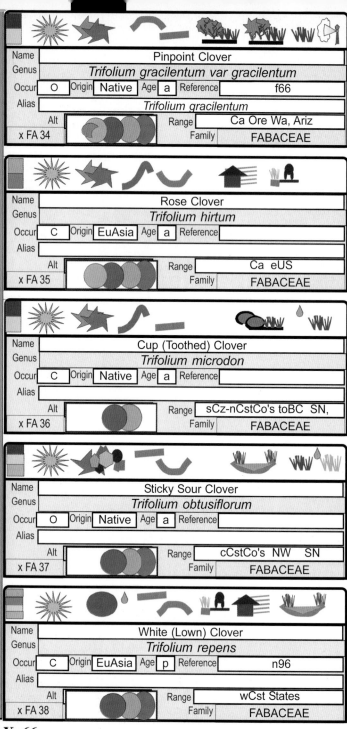

Name		Pinpoint Clover
Genus		*Trifolium gracilentum var gracilentum*
Occur	O	Origin Native Age a Reference f66
Alias		*Trifolium gracilentum*
Alt		Range Ca Ore Wa, Ariz
x FA 34		Family FABACEAE

Name		Rose Clover
Genus		*Trifolium hirtum*
Occur	C	Origin EuAsia Age a Reference
Alias		
Alt		Range Ca eUS
x FA 35		Family FABACEAE

Name		Cup (Toothed) Clover
Genus		*Trifolium microdon*
Occur	C	Origin Native Age a Reference
Alias		
Alt		Range sCz-nCstCo's toBC SN,
x FA 36		Family FABACEAE

Name		Sticky Sour Clover
Genus		*Trifolium obtusiflorum*
Occur	O	Origin Native Age a Reference
Alias		
Alt		Range cCstCo's NW SN
x FA 37		Family FABACEAE

Name		White (Lown) Clover
Genus		*Trifolium repens*
Occur	C	Origin EuAsia Age p Reference n96
Alias		
Alt		Range wCst States
x FA 38		Family FABACEAE

X 66

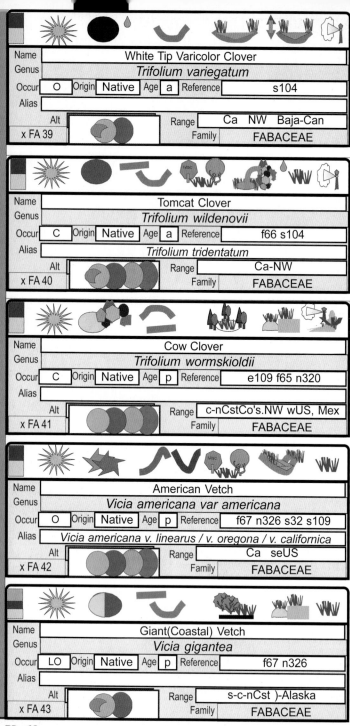

Name	White Tip Varicolor Clover
Genus	*Trifolium variegatum*
Occur	O	Origin	Native	Age	a	Reference	s104
Alias	
Alt		Range	Ca NW Baja-Can
x FA 39		Family	FABACEAE

Name	Tomcat Clover
Genus	*Trifolium wildenovii*
Occur	C	Origin	Native	Age	a	Reference	f66 s104
Alias	*Trifolium tridentatum*
Alt		Range	Ca-NW
x FA 40		Family	FABACEAE

Name	Cow Clover
Genus	*Trifolium wormskioldii*
Occur	C	Origin	Native	Age	p	Reference	e109 f65 n320
Alias	
Alt		Range	c-nCstCo's.NW wUS, Mex
x FA 41		Family	FABACEAE

Name	American Vetch
Genus	*Vicia americana var americana*
Occur	O	Origin	Native	Age	p	Reference	f67 n326 s32 s109
Alias	*Vicia americana v. linearus / v. oregona / v. californica*
Alt		Range	Ca seUS
x FA 42		Family	FABACEAE

Name	Giant(Coastal) Vetch
Genus	*Vicia gigantea*
Occur	LO	Origin	Native	Age	p	Reference	f67 n326
Alias	
Alt		Range	s-c-nCst)-Alaska
x FA 43		Family	FABACEAE

X 68

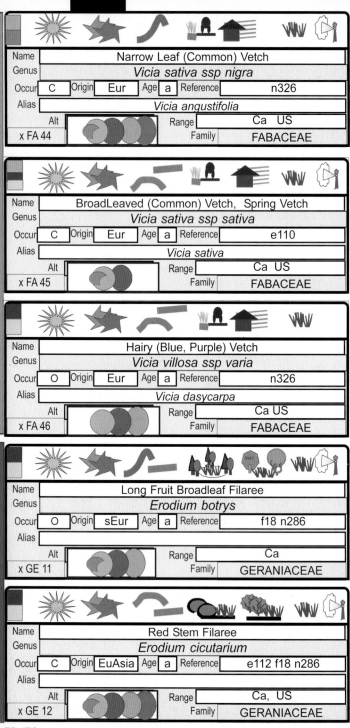

Name	Narrow Leaf (Common) Vetch
Genus	*Vicia sativa ssp nigra*
Occur	C · Origin Eur · Age a · Reference n326
Alias	*Vicia angustifolia*
Alt	Range Ca US
x FA 44	Family FABACEAE

Name	BroadLeaved (Common) Vetch, Spring Vetch
Genus	*Vicia sativa ssp sativa*
Occur	C · Origin Eur · Age a · Reference e110
Alias	*Vicia sativa*
Alt	Range Ca US
x FA 45	Family FABACEAE

Name	Hairy (Blue, Purple) Vetch
Genus	*Vicia villosa ssp varia*
Occur	O · Origin Eur · Age a · Reference n326
Alias	*Vicia dasycarpa*
Alt	Range Ca US
x FA 46	Family FABACEAE

Name	Long Fruit Broadleaf Filaree
Genus	*Erodium botrys*
Occur	O · Origin sEur · Age a · Reference f18 n286
Alias	
Alt	Range Ca
x GE 11	Family GERANIACEAE

Name	Red Stem Filaree
Genus	*Erodium cicutarium*
Occur	C · Origin EuAsia · Age a · Reference e112 f18 n286
Alias	
Alt	Range Ca, US
x GE 12	Family GERANIACEAE

X 70

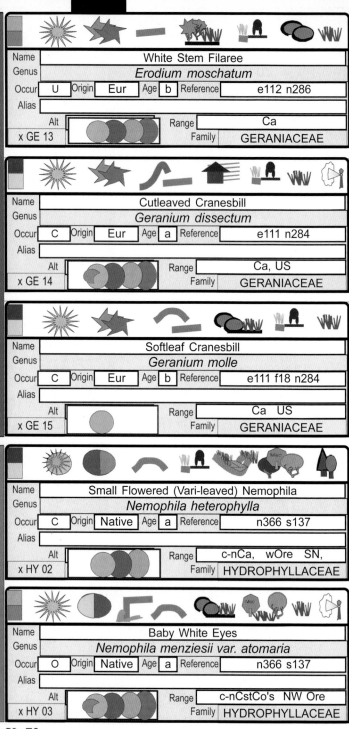

White Stem Filaree

Name		White Stem Filaree			
Genus		*Erodium moschatum*			
Occur	U	Origin	Eur	Age	b	Reference	e112 n286
Alias					
Alt		Range	Ca		
x GE 13		Family	GERANIACEAE		

Cutleaved Cranesbill

Name		Cutleaved Cranesbill			
Genus		*Geranium dissectum*			
Occur	C	Origin	Eur	Age	a	Reference	e111 n284
Alias					
Alt		Range	Ca, US		
x GE 14		Family	GERANIACEAE		

Softleaf Cranesbill

Name		Softleaf Cranesbill			
Genus		*Geranium molle*			
Occur	C	Origin	Eur	Age	b	Reference	e111 f18 n284
Alias					
Alt		Range	Ca US		
x GE 15		Family	GERANIACEAE		

Small Flowered (Vari-leaved) Nemophila

Name		Small Flowered (Vari-leaved) Nemophila			
Genus		*Nemophila heterophylla*			
Occur	C	Origin	Native	Age	a	Reference	n366 s137
Alias					
Alt		Range	c-nCa, wOre SN,		
x HY 02		Family	HYDROPHYLLACEAE		

Baby White Eyes

Name		Baby White Eyes			
Genus		*Nemophila menziesii var. atomaria*			
Occur	O	Origin	Native	Age	a	Reference	n366 s137
Alias					
Alt		Range	c-nCstCo's NW Ore		
x HY 03		Family	HYDROPHYLLACEAE		

X 72

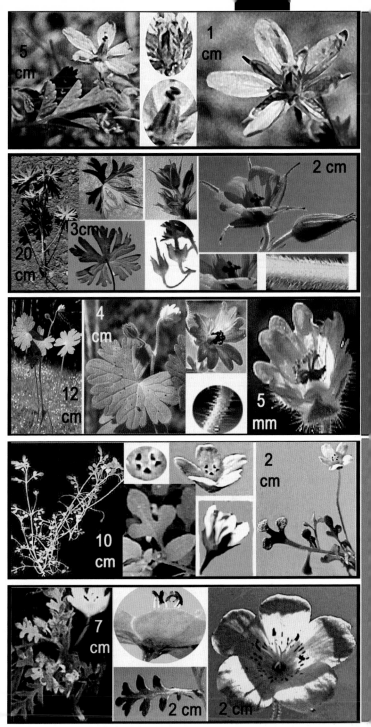

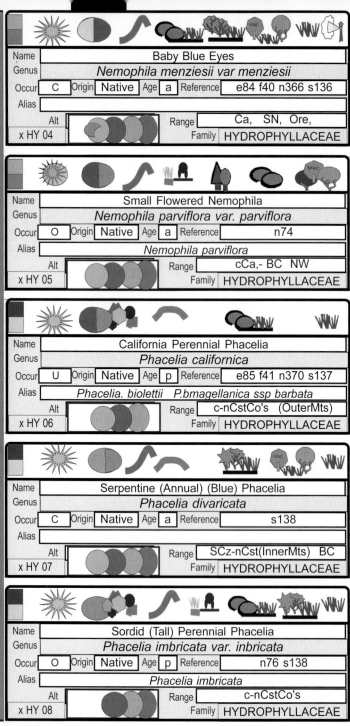

Name	Baby Blue Eyes
Genus	*Nemophila menziesii var menziesii*
Occur	C	Origin	Native	Age	a	Reference	e84 f40 n366 s136
Alias	
Alt		Range	Ca, SN, Ore,
x HY 04		Family	HYDROPHYLLACEAE

Name	Small Flowered Nemophila
Genus	*Nemophila parviflora var. parviflora*
Occur	O	Origin	Native	Age	a	Reference	n74
Alias	*Nemophila parviflora*
Alt		Range	cCa,- BC NW
x HY 05		Family	HYDROPHYLLACEAE

Name	California Perennial Phacelia
Genus	*Phacelia californica*
Occur	U	Origin	Native	Age	p	Reference	e85 f41 n370 s137
Alias	*Phacelia. bioletti* *P.bmagellanica ssp barbata*
Alt		Range	c-nCstCo's (OuterMts)
x HY 06		Family	HYDROPHYLLACEAE

Name	Serpentine (Annual) (Blue) Phacelia
Genus	*Phacelia divaricata*
Occur	C	Origin	Native	Age	a	Reference	s138
Alias	
Alt		Range	SCz-nCst(InnerMts) BC
x HY 07		Family	HYDROPHYLLACEAE

Name	Sordid (Tall) Perennial Phacelia
Genus	*Phacelia imbricata var. inbricata*
Occur	O	Origin	Native	Age	p	Reference	n76 s138
Alias	*Phacelia imbricata*
Alt		Range	c-nCstCo's
x HY 08		Family	HYDROPHYLLACEAE

X 74

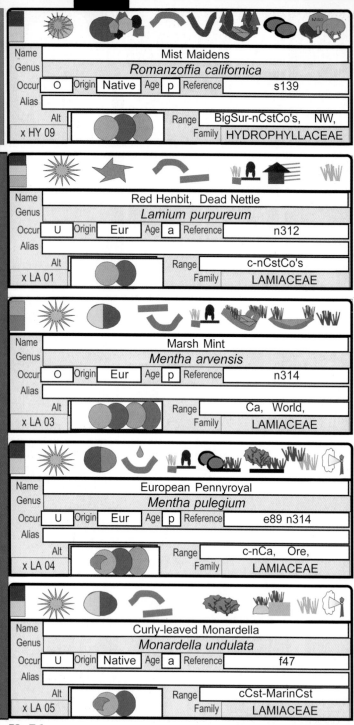

Name	Mist Maidens
Genus	*Romanzoffia californica*
Occur	O Origin Native Age p Reference s139
Alias	
Alt	Range BigSur-nCstCo's, NW,
x HY 09	Family HYDROPHYLLACEAE

Name	Red Henbit, Dead Nettle
Genus	*Lamium purpureum*
Occur	U Origin Eur Age a Reference n312
Alias	
Alt	Range c-nCstCo's
x LA 01	Family LAMIACEAE

Name	Marsh Mint
Genus	*Mentha arvensis*
Occur	O Origin Eur Age p Reference n314
Alias	
Alt	Range Ca, World,
x LA 03	Family LAMIACEAE

Name	European Pennyroyal
Genus	*Mentha pulegium*
Occur	U Origin Eur Age p Reference e89 n314
Alias	
Alt	Range c-nCa, Ore,
x LA 04	Family LAMIACEAE

Name	Curly-leaved Monardella
Genus	*Monardella undulata*
Occur	U Origin Native Age a Reference f47
Alias	
Alt	Range cCst-MarinCst
x LA 05	Family LAMIACEAE

X 76

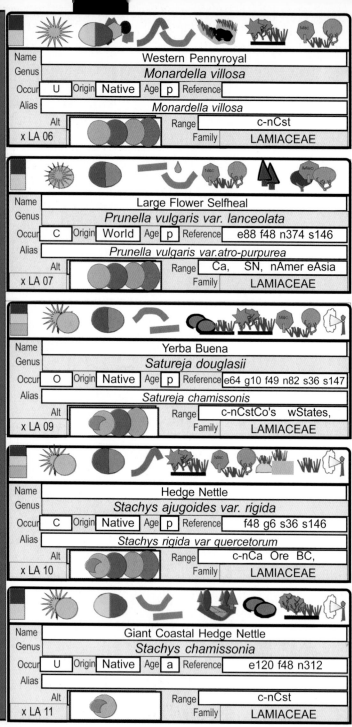

Name	Western Pennyroyal
Genus	*Monardella villosa*
Occur	U	Origin	Native	Age	p	Reference	
Alias	*Monardella villosa*
Alt		Range	c-nCst
x LA 06		Family	LAMIACEAE

Name	Large Flower Selfheal
Genus	*Prunella vulgaris var. lanceolata*
Occur	C	Origin	World	Age	p	Reference	e88 f48 n374 s146
Alias	*Prunella vulgaris var.atro-purpurea*
Alt		Range	Ca, SN, nAmer eAsia
x LA 07		Family	LAMIACEAE

Name	Yerba Buena
Genus	*Satureja douglasii*
Occur	O	Origin	Native	Age	p	Reference	e64 g10 f49 n82 s36 s147
Alias	*Satureja chamissonis*
Alt		Range	c-nCstCo's wStates,
x LA 09		Family	LAMIACEAE

Name	Hedge Nettle
Genus	*Stachys ajugoides var. rigida*
Occur	C	Origin	Native	Age	p	Reference	f48 g6 s36 s146
Alias	*Stachys rigida var quercetorum*
Alt		Range	c-nCa Ore BC,
x LA 10		Family	LAMIACEAE

Name	Giant Coastal Hedge Nettle
Genus	*Stachys chamissonia*
Occur	U	Origin	Native	Age	a	Reference	e120 f48 n312
Alias	
Alt		Range	c-nCst
x LA 11		Family	LAMIACEAE

X 78

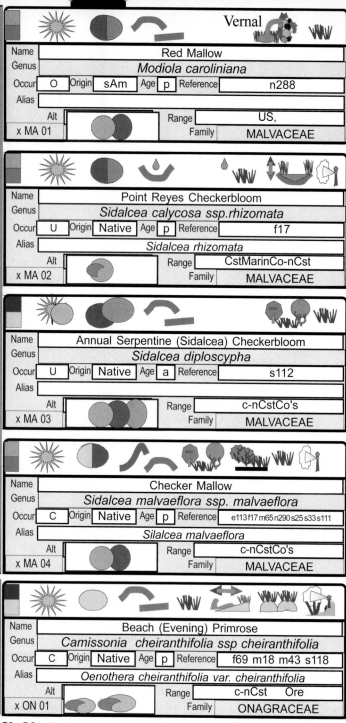

Vernal

Name	Red Mallow
Genus	*Modiola caroliniana*
Occur	O	Origin	sAm	Age	p	Reference	n288
Alias	
Alt		Range	US,
x MA 01		Family	MALVACEAE

Name	Point Reyes Checkerbloom
Genus	*Sidalcea calycosa ssp.rhizomata*
Occur	U	Origin	Native	Age	p	Reference	f17
Alias	*Sidalcea rhizomata*
Alt		Range	CstMarinCo-nCst
x MA 02		Family	MALVACEAE

Name	Annual Serpentine (Sidalcea) Checkerbloom
Genus	*Sidalcea diploscypha*
Occur	U	Origin	Native	Age	a	Reference	s112
Alias	
Alt		Range	c-nCstCo's
x MA 03		Family	MALVACEAE

Name	Checker Mallow
Genus	*Sidalcea malvaeflora ssp. malvaeflora*
Occur	C	Origin	Native	Age	p	Reference	e113 f17 m65 n290 s25 s33 s111
Alias	*Silalcea malvaeflora*
Alt		Range	c-nCstCo's
x MA 04		Family	MALVACEAE

Name	Beach (Evening) Primrose
Genus	*Camissonia cheiranthifolia ssp cheiranthifolia*
Occur	C	Origin	Native	Age	p	Reference	f69 m18 m43 s118
Alias	*Oenothera cheiranthifolia var. cheiranthifolia*
Alt		Range	c-nCst Ore
x ON 01		Family	ONAGRACEAE

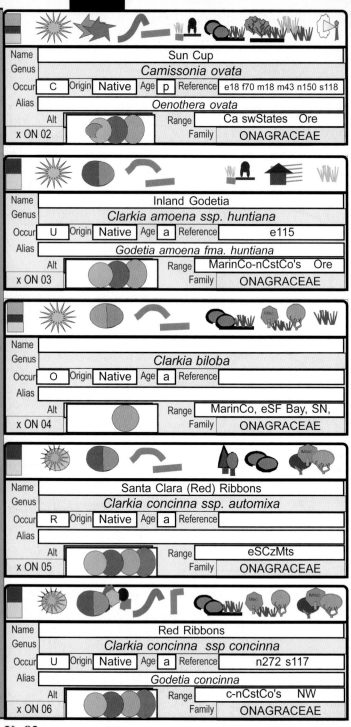

Name	Sun Cup
Genus	*Camissonia ovata*
Occur	C Origin Native Age p Reference e18 f70 m18 m43 n150 s118
Alias	*Oenothera ovata*
Alt	Range Ca swStates Ore
x ON 02	Family ONAGRACEAE

Name	Inland Godetia
Genus	*Clarkia amoena ssp. huntiana*
Occur	U Origin Native Age a Reference e115
Alias	*Godetia amoena fma. huntiana*
Alt	Range MarinCo-nCstCo's Ore
x ON 03	Family ONAGRACEAE

Name	
Genus	*Clarkia biloba*
Occur	O Origin Native Age a Reference
Alias	
Alt	Range MarinCo, eSF Bay, SN,
x ON 04	Family ONAGRACEAE

Name	Santa Clara (Red) Ribbons
Genus	*Clarkia concinna ssp. automixa*
Occur	R Origin Native Age a Reference
Alias	
Alt	Range eSCzMts
x ON 05	Family ONAGRACEAE

Name	Red Ribbons
Genus	*Clarkia concinna ssp concinna*
Occur	U Origin Native Age a Reference n272 s117
Alias	*Godetia concinna*
Alt	Range c-nCstCo's NW
x ON 06	Family ONAGRACEAE

X 82

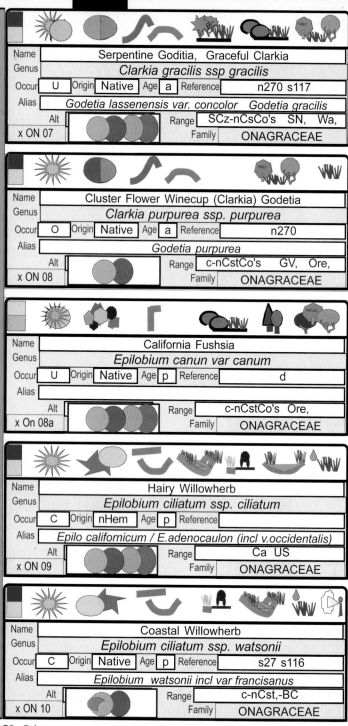

Name	Serpentine Goditia, Graceful Clarkia				
Genus	*Clarkia gracilis ssp gracilis*				
Occur	U	Origin Native	Age a	Reference	n270 s117
Alias	*Godetia lassenensis var. concolor Godetia gracilis*				
Alt			Range	SCz-nCsCo's SN, Wa,	
x ON 07			Family	ONAGRACEAE	

Name	Cluster Flower Winecup (Clarkia) Godetia				
Genus	*Clarkia purpurea ssp. purpurea*				
Occur	O	Origin Native	Age a	Reference	n270
Alias	*Godetia purpurea*				
Alt			Range	c-nCstCo's GV, Ore,	
x ON 08			Family	ONAGRACEAE	

Name	California Fushsia				
Genus	*Epilobium canun var canum*				
Occur	U	Origin Native	Age p	Reference	d
Alias					
Alt			Range	c-nCstCo's Ore,	
x On 08a			Family	ONAGRACEAE	

Name	Hairy Willowherb				
Genus	*Epilobium ciliatum ssp. ciliatum*				
Occur	C	Origin nHem	Age p	Reference	
Alias	*Epilo californicum / E.adenocaulon (incl v.occidentalis)*				
Alt			Range	Ca US	
x ON 09			Family	ONAGRACEAE	

Name	Coastal Willowherb				
Genus	*Epilobium ciliatum ssp. watsonii*				
Occur	C	Origin Native	Age p	Reference	s27 s116
Alias	*Epilobium watsonii incl var francisanus*				
Alt			Range	c-nCst,-BC	
x ON 10			Family	ONAGRACEAE	

X 84

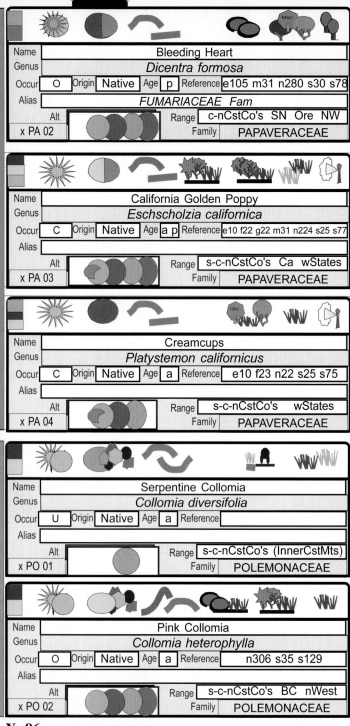

Name		Bleeding Heart
Genus		*Dicentra formosa*
Occur	O	Origin Native Age p Reference e105 m31 n280 s30 s78
Alias		*FUMARIACEAE Fam*
	Alt	Range c-nCstCo's SN Ore NW
x PA 02		Family PAPAVERACEAE

Name		California Golden Poppy
Genus		*Eschscholzia californica*
Occur	C	Origin Native Age a p Reference e10 f22 g22 m31 n224 s25 s77
Alias		
	Alt	Range s-c-nCstCo's Ca wStates
x PA 03		Family PAPAVERACEAE

Name		Creamcups
Genus		*Platystemon californicus*
Occur	C	Origin Native Age a Reference e10 f23 n22 s25 s75
Alias		
	Alt	Range s-c-nCstCo's wStates
x PA 04		Family PAPAVERACEAE

Name		Serpentine Collomia
Genus		*Collomia diversifolia*
Occur	U	Origin Native Age a Reference
Alias		
	Alt	Range s-c-nCstCo's (InnerCstMts)
x PO 01		Family POLEMONACEAE

Name		Pink Collomia
Genus		*Collomia heterophylla*
Occur	O	Origin Native Age a Reference n306 s35 s129
Alias		
	Alt	Range s-c-nCstCo's BC nWest
x PO 02		Family POLEMONACEAE

X 86

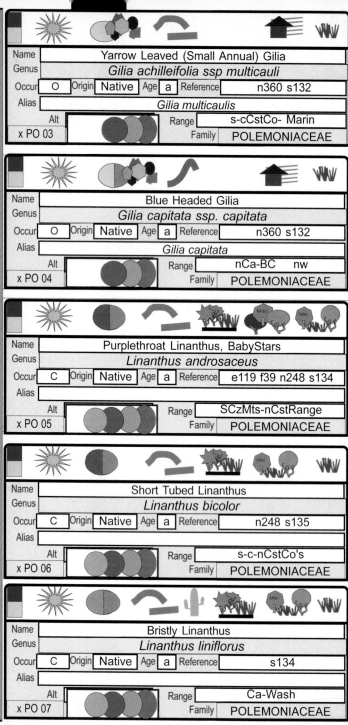

Name	Yarrow Leaved (Small Annual) Gilia
Genus	*Gilia achilleifolia ssp multicauli*
Occur	O	Origin	Native	Age	a	Reference	n360 s132
Alias	*Gilia multicaulis*
Alt		Range	s-cCstCo- Marin
x PO 03		Family	POLEMONIACEAE

Name	Blue Headed Gilia
Genus	*Gilia capitata ssp. capitata*
Occur	O	Origin	Native	Age	a	Reference	n360 s132
Alias	*Gilia capitata*
Alt		Range	nCa-BC nw
x PO 04		Family	POLEMONIACEAE

Name	Purplethroat Linanthus, BabyStars
Genus	*Linanthus androsaceus*
Occur	C	Origin	Native	Age	a	Reference	e119 f39 n248 s134
Alias	
Alt		Range	SCzMts-nCstRange
x PO 05		Family	POLEMONIACEAE

Name	Short Tubed Linanthus
Genus	*Linanthus bicolor*
Occur	C	Origin	Native	Age	a	Reference	n248 s135
Alias	
Alt		Range	s-c-nCstCo's
x PO 06		Family	POLEMONIACEAE

Name	Bristly Linanthus
Genus	*Linanthus liniflorus*
Occur	C	Origin	Native	Age	a	Reference	s134
Alias	
Alt		Range	Ca-Wash
x PO 07		Family	POLEMONIACEAE

X 88

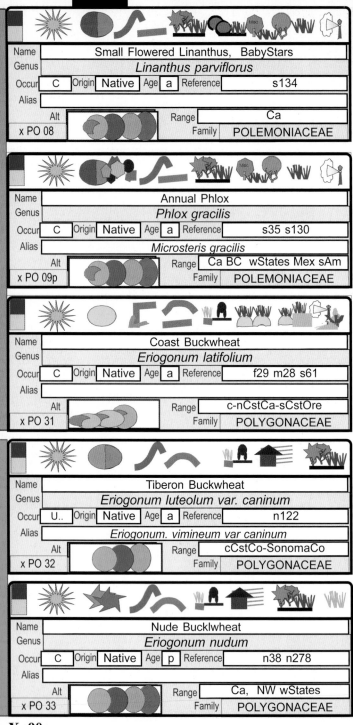

Name	Small Flowered Linanthus, BabyStars
Genus	*Linanthus parviflorus*
Occur	C	Origin	Native	Age	a	Reference	s134
Alias	
Alt		Range	Ca
x PO 08		Family	POLEMONIACEAE

Name	Annual Phlox
Genus	*Phlox gracilis*
Occur	C	Origin	Native	Age	a	Reference	s35 s130
Alias	*Microsteris gracilis*
Alt		Range	Ca BC wStates Mex sAm
x PO 09p		Family	POLEMONIACEAE

Name	Coast Buckwheat
Genus	*Eriogonum latifolium*
Occur	C	Origin	Native	Age	a	Reference	f29 m28 s61
Alias	
Alt		Range	c-nCstCa-sCstOre
x PO 31		Family	POLYGONACEAE

Name	Tiberon Buckwheat
Genus	*Eriogonum luteolum var. caninum*
Occur	U..	Origin	Native	Age	a	Reference	n122
Alias	*Eriogonum. vimineum var caninum*
Alt		Range	cCstCo-SonomaCo
x PO 32		Family	POLYGONACEAE

Name	Nude Bucklwheat
Genus	*Eriogonum nudum*
Occur	C	Origin	Native	Age	p	Reference	n38 n278
Alias	
Alt		Range	Ca, NW wStates
x PO 33		Family	POLYGONACEAE

X 90

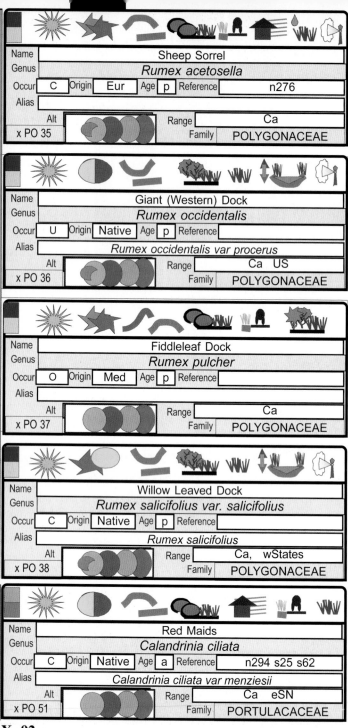

Name	Sheep Sorrel
Genus	*Rumex acetosella*
Occur	C	Origin	Eur	Age	p	Reference	n276
Alias	
Alt	Range	Ca
x PO 35	Family	POLYGONACEAE

Name	Giant (Western) Dock
Genus	*Rumex occidentalis*
Occur	U	Origin	Native	Age	p	Reference	
Alias	*Rumex occidentalis var procerus*
Alt	Range	Ca US
x PO 36	Family	POLYGONACEAE

Name	Fiddleleaf Dock
Genus	*Rumex pulcher*
Occur	O	Origin	Med	Age	p	Reference	
Alias	
Alt	Range	Ca
x PO 37	Family	POLYGONACEAE

Name	Willow Leaved Dock
Genus	*Rumex salicifolius var. salicifolius*
Occur	C	Origin	Native	Age	p	Reference	
Alias	*Rumex salicifolius*
Alt	Range	Ca, wStates
x PO 38	Family	POLYGONACEAE

Name	Red Maids
Genus	*Calandrinia ciliata*
Occur	C	Origin	Native	Age	a	Reference	n294 s25 s62
Alias	*Calandrinia ciliata var menziesii*
Alt	Range	Ca eSN
x PO 51	Family	PORTULACACEAE

X 92

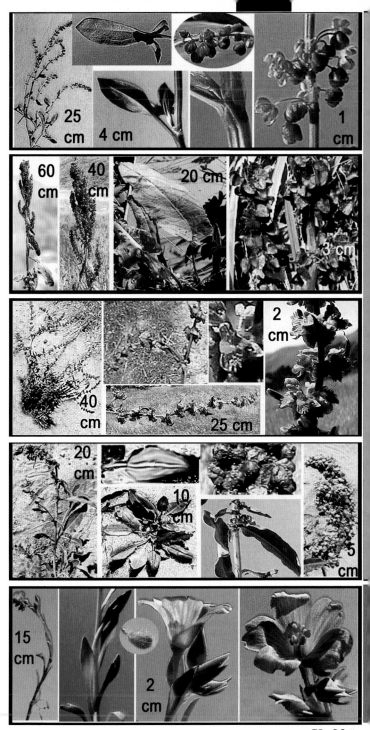

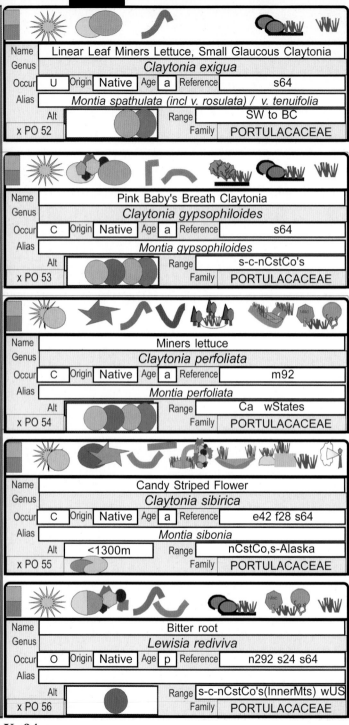

Name	Linear Leaf Miners Lettuce, Small Glaucous Claytonia
Genus	*Claytonia exigua*
Occur	U **Origin** Native **Age** a **Reference** s64
Alias	*Montia spathulata (incl v. rosulata) / v. tenuifolia*
Alt	**Range** SW to BC
x PO 52	**Family** PORTULACACEAE

Name	Pink Baby's Breath Claytonia
Genus	*Claytonia gypsophiloides*
Occur	C **Origin** Native **Age** a **Reference** s64
Alias	*Montia gypsophiloides*
Alt	**Range** s-c-nCstCo's
x PO 53	**Family** PORTULACACEAE

Name	Miners lettuce
Genus	*Claytonia perfoliata*
Occur	C **Origin** Native **Age** a **Reference** m92
Alias	*Montia perfoliata*
Alt	**Range** Ca wStates
x PO 54	**Family** PORTULACACEAE

Name	Candy Striped Flower
Genus	*Claytonia sibirica*
Occur	C **Origin** Native **Age** a **Reference** e42 f28 s64
Alias	*Montia sibonia*
Alt	<1300m **Range** nCstCo,s-Alaska
x PO 55	**Family** PORTULACACEAE

Name	Bitter root
Genus	*Lewisia rediviva*
Occur	O **Origin** Native **Age** p **Reference** n292 s24 s64
Alias	
Alt	**Range** s-c-nCstCo's(InnerMts) wUS
x PO 56	**Family** PORTULACACEAE

X 94

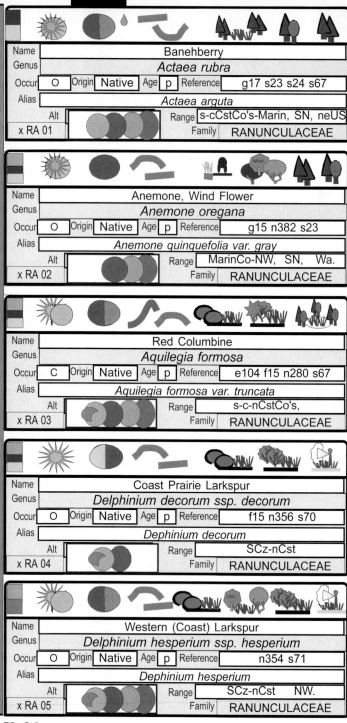

Name	Banehberry
Genus	*Actaea rubra*
Occur	O	Origin	Native	Age	p	Reference	g17 s23 s24 s67
Alias	*Actaea arguta*
Alt	Range	s-cCstCo's-Marin, SN, neUS
x RA 01	Family	RANUNCULACEAE

Name	Anemone, Wind Flower
Genus	*Anemone oregana*
Occur	O	Origin	Native	Age	p	Reference	g15 n382 s23
Alias	*Anemone quinquefolia var. gray*
Alt	Range	MarinCo-NW, SN, Wa.
x RA 02	Family	RANUNCULACEAE

Name	Red Columbine
Genus	*Aquilegia formosa*
Occur	C	Origin	Native	Age	p	Reference	e104 f15 n280 s67
Alias	*Aquilegia formosa var. truncata*
Alt	Range	s-c-nCstCo's,
x RA 03	Family	RANUNCULACEAE

Name	Coast Prairie Larkspur
Genus	*Delphinium decorum ssp. decorum*
Occur	O	Origin	Native	Age	p	Reference	f15 n356 s70
Alias	*Dephinium decorum*
Alt	Range	SCz-nCst
x RA 04	Family	RANUNCULACEAE

Name	Western (Coast) Larkspur
Genus	*Delphinium hesperium ssp. hesperium*
Occur	O	Origin	Native	Age	p	Reference	n354 s71
Alias	*Dephinium hesperium*
Alt	Range	SCz-nCst NW.
x RA 05	Family	RANUNCULACEAE

X 96

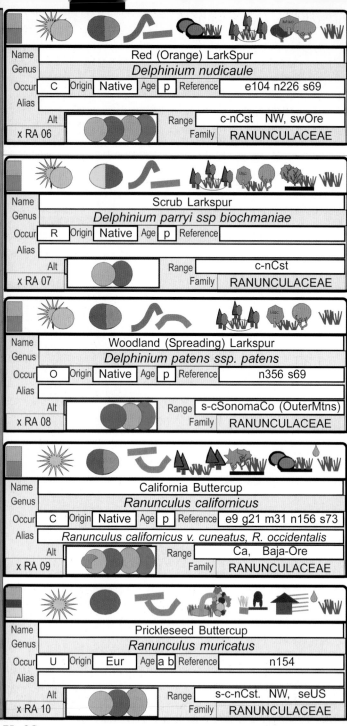

Name	Red (Orange) LarkSpur
Genus	*Delphinium nudicaule*
Occur	C	Origin	Native	Age	p	Reference	e104 n226 s69
Alias	
Alt		Range	c-nCst NW, swOre
x RA 06		Family	RANUNCULACEAE

Name	Scrub Larkspur
Genus	*Delphinium parryi ssp biochmaniae*
Occur	R	Origin	Native	Age	p	Reference	
Alias	
Alt		Range	c-nCst
x RA 07		Family	RANUNCULACEAE

Name	Woodland (Spreading) Larkspur
Genus	*Delphinium patens ssp. patens*
Occur	O	Origin	Native	Age	p	Reference	n356 s69
Alias	
Alt		Range	s-cSonomaCo (OuterMtns)
x RA 08		Family	RANUNCULACEAE

Name	California Buttercup
Genus	*Ranunculus californicus*
Occur	C	Origin	Native	Age	p	Reference	e9 g21 m31 n156 s73
Alias	*Ranunculus californicus v. cuneatus, R. occidentalis*
Alt		Range	Ca, Baja-Ore
x RA 09		Family	RANUNCULACEAE

Name	Prickleseed Buttercup
Genus	*Ranunculus muricatus*
Occur	U	Origin	Eur	Age	a b	Reference	n154
Alias	
Alt		Range	s-c-nCst. NW, seUS
x RA 10		Family	RANUNCULACEAE

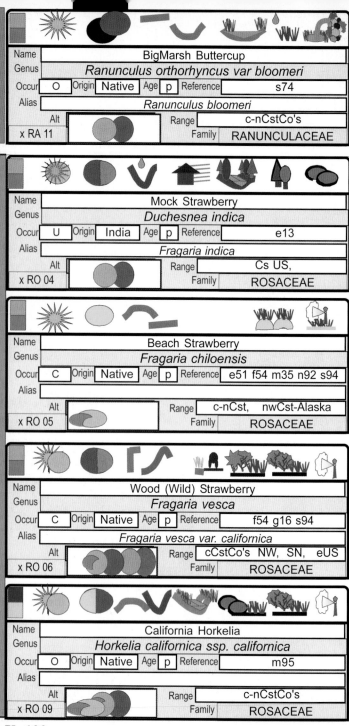

Name	BigMarsh Buttercup
Genus	*Ranunculus orthorhyncus var bloomeri*

Occur	O	Origin	Native	Age	p	Reference	s74

Alias	*Ranunculus bloomeri*

Alt		Range	c-nCstCo's
x RA 11		Family	RANUNCULACEAE

Name	Mock Strawberry
Genus	*Duchesnea indica*

Occur	U	Origin	India	Age	p	Reference	e13

Alias	*Fragaria indica*

Alt		Range	Cs US,
x RO 04		Family	ROSACEAE

Name	Beach Strawberry
Genus	*Fragaria chiloensis*

Occur	C	Origin	Native	Age	p	Reference	e51 f54 m35 n92 s94

Alias	

Alt		Range	c-nCst, nwCst-Alaska
x RO 05		Family	ROSACEAE

Name	Wood (Wild) Strawberry
Genus	*Fragaria vesca*

Occur	C	Origin	Native	Age	p	Reference	f54 g16 s94

Alias	*Fragaria vesca var. californica*

Alt		Range	cCstCo's NW, SN, eUS
x RO 06		Family	ROSACEAE

Name	California Horkelia
Genus	*Horkelia californica ssp. californica*

Occur	O	Origin	Native	Age	p	Reference	m95

Alias	

Alt		Range	c-nCstCo's
x RO 09		Family	ROSACEAE

X 100

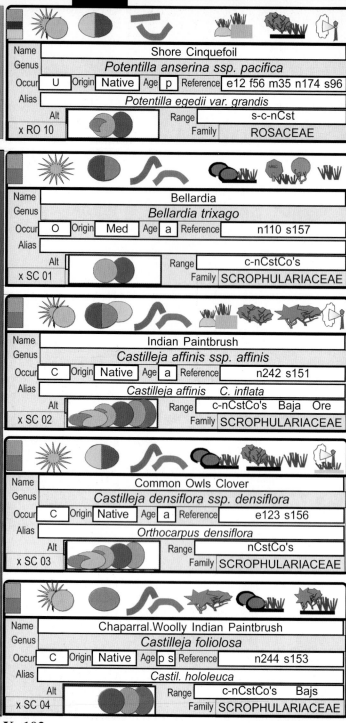

Shore Cinquefoil

Name	Shore Cinquefoil
Genus	*Potentilla anserina ssp. pacifica*
Occur	U	Origin	Native	Age	p	Reference	e12 f56 m35 n174 s96
Alias	*Potentilla egedii var. grandis*

Alt | Range | s-c-nCst
x RO 10 | Family | ROSACEAE

Bellardia

Name	Bellardia
Genus	*Bellardia trixago*
Occur	O	Origin	Med	Age	a	Reference	n110 s157
Alias	

Alt | Range | c-nCstCo's
x SC 01 | Family | SCROPHULARIACEAE

Indian Paintbrush

Name	Indian Paintbrush
Genus	*Castilleja affinis ssp. affinis*
Occur	C	Origin	Native	Age	a	Reference	n242 s151
Alias	*Castilleja affinis C. inflata*

Alt | Range | c-nCstCo's Baja Ore
x SC 02 | Family | SCROPHULARIACEAE

Common Owls Clover

Name	Common Owls Clover
Genus	*Castilleja densiflora ssp. densiflora*
Occur	C	Origin	Native	Age	a	Reference	e123 s156
Alias	*Orthocarpus densiflora*

Alt | Range | nCstCo's
x SC 03 | Family | SCROPHULARIACEAE

Chaparral.Woolly Indian Paintbrush

Name	Chaparral.Woolly Indian Paintbrush
Genus	*Castilleja foliolosa*
Occur	C	Origin	Native	Age	p s	Reference	n244 s153
Alias	*Castil. hololeuca*

Alt | Range | c-nCstCo's Bajs
x SC 04 | Family | SCROPHULARIACEAE

X 102

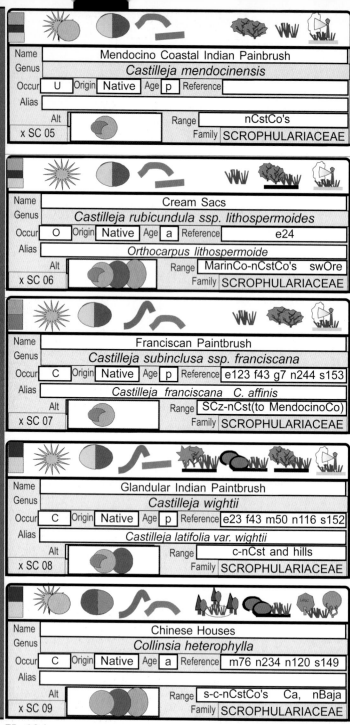

Name	Mendocino Coastal Indian Painbrush
Genus	*Castilleja mendocinensis*

Occur	U	Origin	Native	Age	p	Reference	

Alias

Alt		Range	nCstCo's
x SC 05		Family	SCROPHULARIACEAE

Name	Cream Sacs
Genus	*Castilleja rubicundula ssp. lithospermoides*

Occur	O	Origin	Native	Age	a	Reference	e24

Alias	*Orthocarpus lithospermoide*

Alt		Range	MarinCo-nCstCo's swOre
x SC 06		Family	SCROPHULARIACEAE

Name	Franciscan Paintbrush
Genus	*Castilleja subinclusa ssp. franciscana*

Occur	C	Origin	Native	Age	p	Reference	e123 f43 g7 n244 s153

Alias	*Castilleja franciscana C. affinis*

Alt		Range	SCz-nCst(to MendocinoCo)
x SC 07		Family	SCROPHULARIACEAE

Name	Glandular Indian Paintbrush
Genus	*Castilleja wightii*

Occur	C	Origin	Native	Age	p	Reference	e23 f43 m50 n116 s152

Alias	*Castilleja latifolia var. wightii*

Alt		Range	c-nCst and hills
x SC 08		Family	SCROPHULARIACEAE

Name	Chinese Houses
Genus	*Collinsia heterophylla*

Occur	C	Origin	Native	Age	a	Reference	m76 n234 n120 s149

Alias

Alt		Range	s-c-nCstCo's Ca, nBaja
x SC 09		Family	SCROPHULARIACEAE

X 104

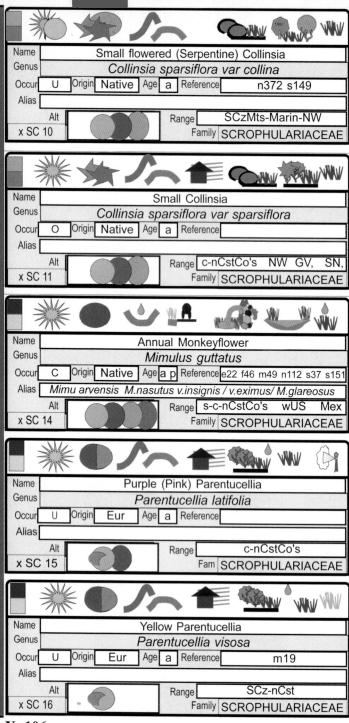

Name	Small flowered (Serpentine) Collinsia
Genus	*Collinsia sparsiflora var collina*
Occur	U	Origin	Native	Age	a	Reference	n372 s149
Alias	
Alt		Range	SCzMts-Marin-NW
x SC 10		Family	SCROPHULARIACEAE

Name	Small Collinsia
Genus	*Collinsia sparsiflora var sparsiflora*
Occur	O	Origin	Native	Age	a	Reference	
Alias	
Alt		Range	c-nCstCo's NW GV, SN,
x SC 11		Family	SCROPHULARIACEAE

Name	Annual Monkeyflower
Genus	*Mimulus guttatus*
Occur	C	Origin	Native	Age	a p	Reference	e22 f46 m49 n112 s37 s151
Alias	*Mimu arvensis M.nasutus v.insignis / v.eximus/ M.glareosus*
Alt		Range	s-c-nCstCo's wUS Mex
x SC 14		Family	SCROPHULARIACEAE

Name	Purple (Pink) Parentucellia
Genus	*Parentucellia latifolia*
Occur	U	Origin	Eur	Age	a	Reference	
Alias	
Alt		Range	c-nCstCo's
x SC 15		Fam	SCROPHULARIACEAE

Name	Yellow Parentucellia
Genus	*Parentucellia visosa*
Occur	U	Origin	Eur	Age	a	Reference	m19
Alias	
Alt		Range	SCz-nCst
x SC 16		Family	SCROPHULARIACEAE

X 106

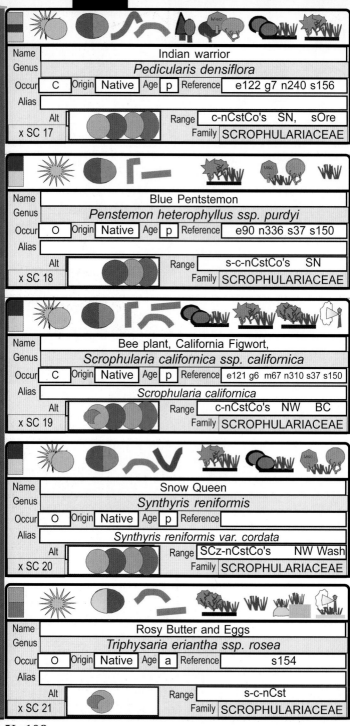

Name	Indian warrior
Genus	*Pedicularis densiflora*
Occur	C — Origin: Native — Age: p — Reference: e122 g7 n240 s156
Alias	
Alt	Range: c-nCstCo's SN, sOre
x SC 17	Family: SCROPHULARIACEAE

Name	Blue Pentstemon
Genus	*Penstemon heterophyllus ssp. purdyi*
Occur	O — Origin: Native — Age: p — Reference: e90 n336 s37 s150
Alias	
Alt	Range: s-c-nCstCo's SN
x SC 18	Family: SCROPHULARIACEAE

Name	Bee plant, California Figwort,
Genus	*Scrophularia californica ssp. californica*
Occur	C — Origin: Native — Age: p — Reference: e121 g6 m67 n310 s37 s150
Alias	*Scrophularia californica*
Alt	Range: c-nCstCo's NW BC
x SC 19	Family: SCROPHULARIACEAE

Name	Snow Queen
Genus	*Synthyris reniformis*
Occur	O — Origin: Native — Age: p — Reference:
Alias	*Synthyris reniformis var. cordata*
Alt	Range: SCz-nCstCo's NW Wash
x SC 20	Family: SCROPHULARIACEAE

Name	Rosy Butter and Eggs
Genus	*Triphysaria eriantha ssp. rosea*
Occur	O — Origin: Native — Age: a — Reference: s154
Alias	
Alt	Range: s-c-nCst
x SC 21	Family: SCROPHULARIACEAE

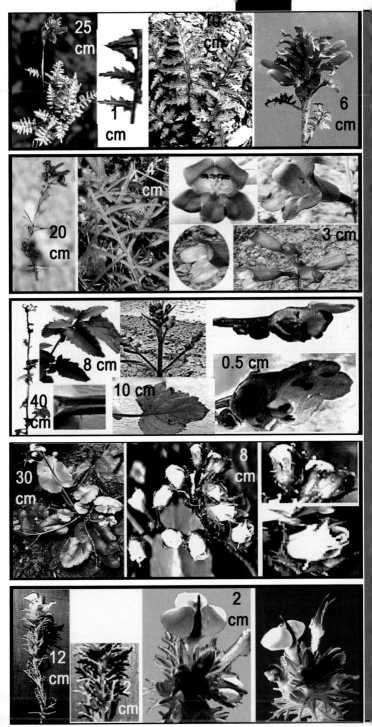

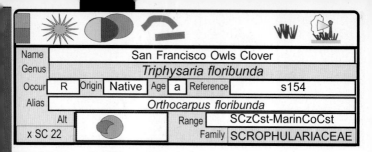

Name	San Francisco Owls Clover
Genus	*Triphysaria floribunda*
Occur	R	Origin	Native	Age	a	Reference	s154
Alias	*Orthocarpus floribunda*

Alt		Range	SCzCst-MarinCoCst
x SC 22		Family	SCROPHULARIACEAE

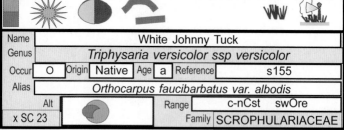

Name	White Johnny Tuck
Genus	*Triphysaria versicolor ssp versicolor*
Occur	O	Origin	Native	Age	a	Reference	s155
Alias	*Orthocarpus faucibarbatus var. albodis*

Alt		Range	c-nCst swOre
x SC 23		Family	SCROPHULARIACEAE

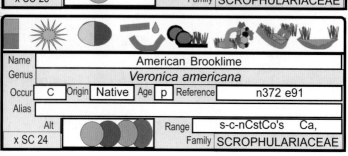

Name	American Brooklime
Genus	*Veronica americana*
Occur	C	Origin	Native	Age	p	Reference	n372 e91
Alias	

Alt		Range	s-c-nCstCo's Ca,
x SC 24		Family	SCROPHULARIACEAE

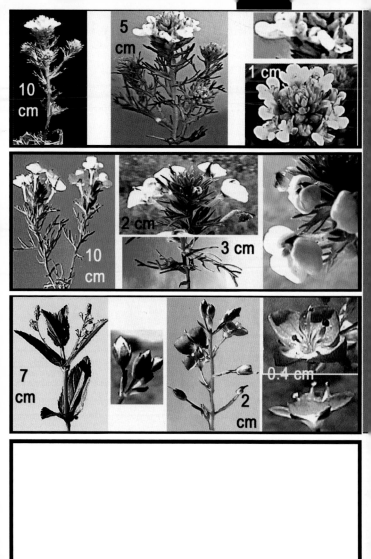

Miscellaneous Non Woody Dicots

These plants are from dicot families which have a jiust a few common species but not a wide selection of local species

Name	Greater Periwinkle				
Genus	*Vinca major*				
Occur	C-Exc.	Origin Eur	Age	Reference	e83 n382
Alias					
Alt			Range	s-c-nCstCo's PLANTED	
x AP 20			Family	APOCYNACEAE	

Name	Elk Clover, California Spikenard				
Genus	*Aralia californica*				
Occur	C	Origin Eur	Age p	Reference	g18 n64
Alias					
Alt			Range	c-nCstCo's-Ore	
x AR 01			Family	ARALIACEAE	

Name	Wild Ginger				
Genus	*Asarum caudatum*				
Occur	O	Origin Native	Age p	Reference	e100 g18 m61 n400 s23
Alias					s59
Alt			Range	BigSur-nCstCo's-BC	
x AR 11n			Family	ARISTOLOCHIACEAE	

Name	Redwood Inside-out Flower				
Genus	*Vancouveria planipetala*				
Occur	C	Origin Native	Age s	Reference	e44 n42 s24 s74
Alias					
Alt			Range	c-nCstCo's Mts (BigS-Ore)	
x BE 03			Family	BERBERIDACEAE	

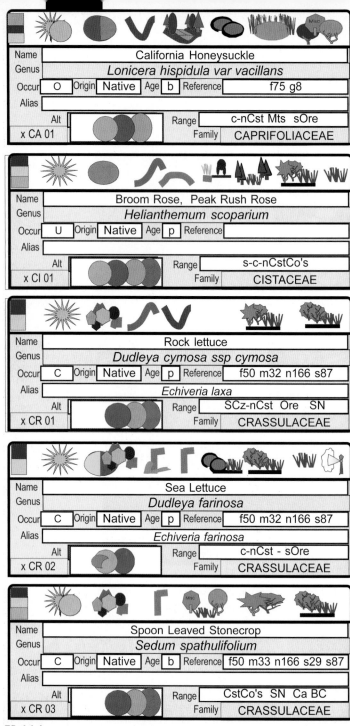

Name	California Honeysuckle	
Genus	*Lonicera hispidula var vacillans*	
Occur	O	Origin	Native	Age	b	Reference	f75 g8
Alias		
Alt		Range	c-nCst Mts sOre
x CA 01		Family	CAPRIFOLIACEAE

Name	Broom Rose, Peak Rush Rose	
Genus	*Helianthemum scoparium*	
Occur	U	Origin	Native	Age	p	Reference	
Alias		
Alt		Range	s-c-nCstCo's
x CI 01		Family	CISTACEAE

Name	Rock lettuce	
Genus	*Dudleya cymosa ssp cymosa*	
Occur	C	Origin	Native	Age	p	Reference	f50 m32 n166 s87
Alias	*Echiveria laxa*	
Alt		Range	SCz-nCst Ore SN
x CR 01		Family	CRASSULACEAE

Name	Sea Lettuce	
Genus	*Dudleya farinosa*	
Occur	C	Origin	Native	Age	p	Reference	f50 m32 n166 s87
Alias	*Echiveria farinosa*	
Alt		Range	c-nCst - sOre
x CR 02		Family	CRASSULACEAE

Name	Spoon Leaved Stonecrop	
Genus	*Sedum spathulifolium*	
Occur	C	Origin	Native	Age	b	Reference	f50 m33 n166 s29 s87
Alias		
Alt		Range	CstCo's SN Ca BC
x CR 03		Family	CRASSULACEAE

X 114

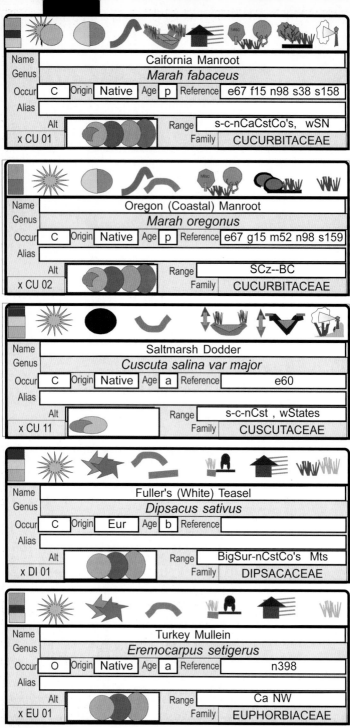

Name	Caifornia Manroot
Genus	*Marah fabaceus*
Occur	C	Origin	Native	Age	p	Reference	e67 f15 n98 s38 s158
Alias	
Alt		Range	s-c-nCaCstCo's, wSN
x CU 01		Family	CUCURBITACEAE

Name	Oregon (Coastal) Manroot
Genus	*Marah oregonus*
Occur	C	Origin	Native	Age	p	Reference	e67 g15 m52 n98 s159
Alias	
Alt		Range	SCz--BC
x CU 02		Family	CUCURBITACEAE

Name	Saltmarsh Dodder
Genus	*Cuscuta salina var major*
Occur	C	Origin	Native	Age	a	Reference	e60
Alias	
Alt		Range	s-c-nCst , wStates
x CU 11		Family	CUSCUTACEAE

Name	Fuller's (White) Teasel
Genus	*Dipsacus sativus*
Occur	C	Origin	Eur	Age	b	Reference	
Alias	
Alt		Range	BigSur-nCstCo's Mts
x DI 01		Family	DIPSACACEAE

Name	Turkey Mullein
Genus	*Eremocarpus setigerus*
Occur	O	Origin	Native	Age	a	Reference	n398
Alias	
Alt		Range	Ca NW
x EU 01		Family	EUPHORBIACEAE

X 116

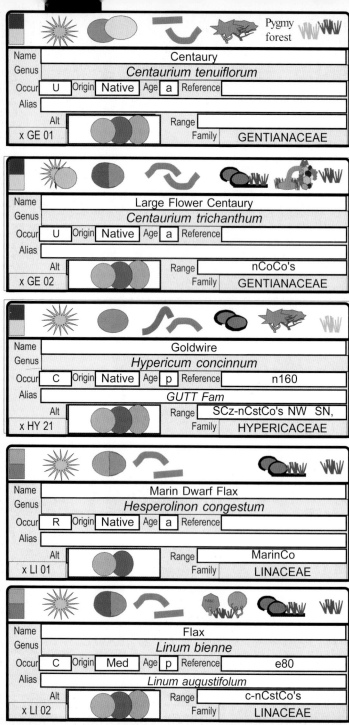

Centaury
Genus: *Centaurium tenuiflorum*
Occur: U | Origin: Native | Age: a | Reference:
Alias:
Alt | Range:
x GE 01 | Family: GENTIANACEAE

Large Flower Centaury
Genus: *Centaurium trichanthum*
Occur: U | Origin: Native | Age: a | Reference:
Alias:
Alt | Range: nCoCo's
x GE 02 | Family: GENTIANACEAE

Goldwire
Genus: *Hypericum concinnum*
Occur: C | Origin: Native | Age: p | Reference: n160
Alias: *GUTT Fam*
Alt | Range: SCz-nCstCo's NW SN,
x HY 21 | Family: HYPERICACEAE

Marin Dwarf Flax
Genus: *Hesperolinon congestum*
Occur: R | Origin: Native | Age: a | Reference:
Alias:
Alt | Range: MarinCo
x LI 01 | Family: LINACEAE

Flax
Genus: *Linum bienne*
Occur: C | Origin: Med | Age: p | Reference: e80
Alias: *Linum augustifolum*
Alt | Range: c-nCstCo's
x LI 02 | Family: LINACEAE

X 118

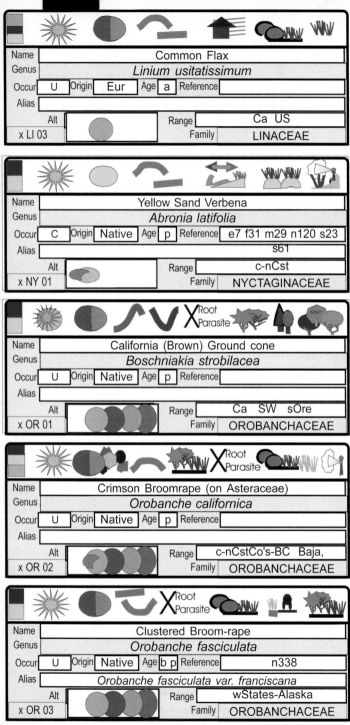

Common Flax

Linium usitatissimum

Occur	U	Origin	Eur	Age	a	Reference	

Alias

Alt		Range	Ca US
x Ll 03		Family	LINACEAE

Yellow Sand Verbena

Abronia latifolia

Occur	C	Origin	Native	Age	p	Reference	e7 f31 m29 n120 s23

Alias s61

Alt		Range	c-nCst
x NY 01		Family	NYCTAGINACEAE

California (Brown) Ground cone

Boschniakia strobilacea

Occur	U	Origin	Native	Age	p	Reference	

Alias

Alt		Range	Ca SW sOre
x OR 01		Family	OROBANCHACEAE

Crimson Broomrape (on Asteraceae)

Orobanche californica

Occur	U	Origin	Native	Age	p	Reference	

Alias

Alt		Range	c-nCstCo's-BC Baja,
x OR 02		Family	OROBANCHACEAE

Clustered Broom-rape

Orobanche fasciculata

Occur	U	Origin	Native	Age	b p	Reference	n338

Alias *Orobanche fasciculata var. franciscana*

Alt		Range	wStates-Alaska
x OR 03		Family	OROBANCHACEAE

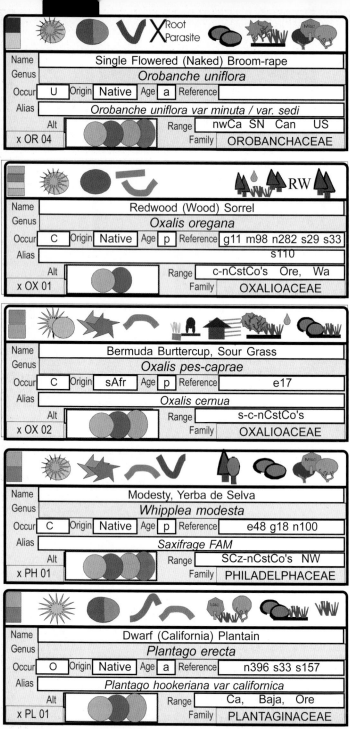

Name	Single Flowered (Naked) Broom-rape
Genus	*Orobanche uniflora*
Occur	U	Origin	Native	Age	a	Reference	
Alias	*Orobanche uniflora var minuta / var. sedi*
Alt		Range	nwCa SN Can US
x OR 04		Family	OROBANCHACEAE

Root Parasite

Name	Redwood (Wood) Sorrel
Genus	*Oxalis oregana*
Occur	C	Origin	Native	Age	p	Reference	g11 m98 n282 s29 s33
Alias	s110
Alt		Range	c-nCstCo's Ore, Wa
x OX 01		Family	OXALIOACEAE

RW

Name	Bermuda Burttercup, Sour Grass
Genus	*Oxalis pes-caprae*
Occur	C	Origin	sAfr	Age	p	Reference	e17
Alias	*Oxalis cernua*
Alt		Range	s-c-nCstCo's
x OX 02		Family	OXALIOACEAE

Name	Modesty, Yerba de Selva
Genus	*Whipplea modesta*
Occur	C	Origin	Native	Age	p	Reference	e48 g18 n100
Alias	*Saxifrage FAM*
Alt		Range	SCz-nCstCo's NW
x PH 01		Family	PHILADELPHACEAE

Name	Dwarf (California) Plantain
Genus	*Plantago erecta*
Occur	O	Origin	Native	Age	a	Reference	n396 s33 s157
Alias	*Plantago hookeriana var californica*
Alt		Range	Ca, Baja, Ore
x PL 01		Family	PLANTAGINACEAE

X 122

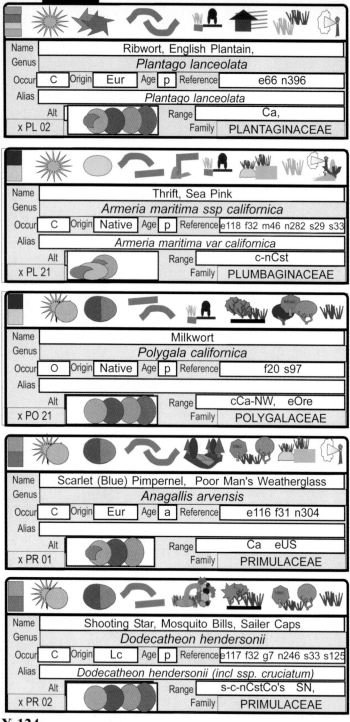

Name	Ribwort, English Plantain,	
Genus	*Plantago lanceolata*	
Occur	C	Origin	Eur	Age	p	Reference	e66 n396
Alias	*Plantago lanceolata*	
Alt		Range	Ca,
x PL 02		Family	PLANTAGINACEAE

Name	Thrift, Sea Pink	
Genus	*Armeria maritima ssp californica*	
Occur	C	Origin	Native	Age	p	Reference	e118 f32 m46 n282 s29 s33
Alias	*Armeria maritima var californica*	
Alt		Range	c-nCst
x PL 21		Family	PLUMBAGINACEAE

Name	Milkwort	
Genus	*Polygala californica*	
Occur	O	Origin	Native	Age	p	Reference	f20 s97
Alias		
Alt		Range	cCa-NW, eOre
x PO 21		Family	POLYGALACEAE

Name	Scarlet (Blue) Pimpernel, Poor Man's Weatherglass	
Genus	*Anagallis arvensis*	
Occur	C	Origin	Eur	Age	a	Reference	e116 f31 n304
Alias		
Alt		Range	Ca eUS
x PR 01		Family	PRIMULACEAE

Name	Shooting Star, Mosquito Bills, Sailer Caps	
Genus	*Dodecatheon hendersonii*	
Occur	C	Origin	Lc	Age	p	Reference	e117 f32 g7 n246 s33 s125
Alias	*Dodecatheon hendersonii (incl ssp. cruciatum)*	
Alt		Range	s-c-nCstCo's SN,
x PR 02		Family	PRIMULACEAE

X 124

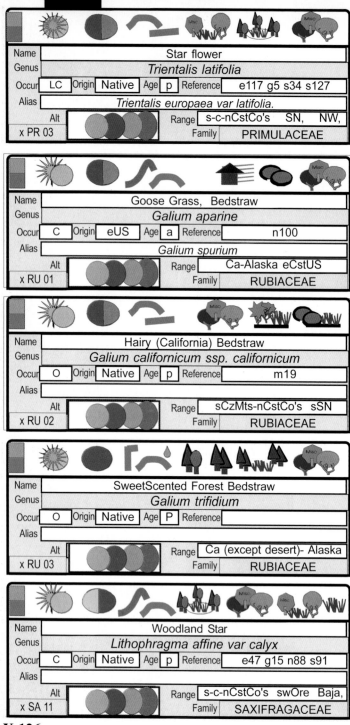

Name Star flower
Genus *Trientalis latifolia*
Occur LC **Origin** Native **Age** p **Reference** e117 g5 s34 s127
Alias *Trientalis europaea var latifolia.*
Alt
x PR 03 **Range** s-c-nCstCo's SN, NW,
Family PRIMULACEAE

Name Goose Grass, Bedstraw
Genus *Galium aparine*
Occur C **Origin** eUS **Age** a **Reference** n100
Alias *Galium spurium*
Alt
x RU 01 **Range** Ca-Alaska eCstUS
Family RUBIACEAE

Name Hairy (California) Bedstraw
Genus *Galium californicum ssp. californicum*
Occur O **Origin** Native **Age** p **Reference** m19
Alias
Alt
x RU 02 **Range** sCzMts-nCstCo's sSN
Family RUBIACEAE

Name SweetScented Forest Bedstraw
Genus *Galium trifidium*
Occur O **Origin** Native **Age** P **Reference**
Alias
Alt
x RU 03 **Range** Ca (except desert)- Alaska
Family RUBIACEAE

Name Woodland Star
Genus *Lithophragma affine var calyx*
Occur C **Origin** Native **Age** p **Reference** e47 g15 n88 s91
Alias
Alt
x SA 11 **Range** s-c-nCstCo's swOre Baja,
Family SAXIFRAGACEAE

X 126

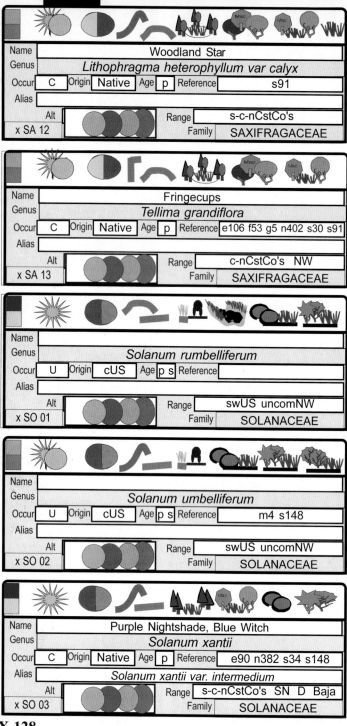

Name	Woodland Star
Genus	*Lithophragma heterophyllum var calyx*
Occur	C	Origin	Native	Age	p	Reference	s91
Alias	
Alt		Range	s-c-nCstCo's
x SA 12		Family	SAXIFRAGACEAE

Name	Fringecups
Genus	*Tellima grandiflora*
Occur	C	Origin	Native	Age	p	Reference	e106 f53 g5 n402 s30 s91
Alias	
Alt		Range	c-nCstCo's NW
x SA 13		Family	SAXIFRAGACEAE

Name	
Genus	*Solanum rumbelliferum*
Occur	U	Origin	cUS	Age	p s	Reference	
Alias	
Alt		Range	swUS uncomNW
x SO 01		Family	SOLANACEAE

Name	
Genus	*Solanum umbelliferum*
Occur	U	Origin	cUS	Age	p s	Reference	m4 s148
Alias	
Alt		Range	swUS uncomNW
x SO 02		Family	SOLANACEAE

Name	Purple Nightshade, Blue Witch
Genus	*Solanum xantii*
Occur	C	Origin	Native	Age	p	Reference	e90 n382 s34 s148
Alias	*Solanum xantii var. intermedium*
Alt		Range	s-c-nCstCo's SN D Baja
x SO 03		Family	SOLANACEAE

X 128

40x2
cm

3
cm

1
cm

60
cm

30
cm

1 cm

1
cm

8 cm

50
cm

30
cm-

2 cm

3 cm

1.5
M

20
cm

5
cm

30
cm

4 cm

2 cm

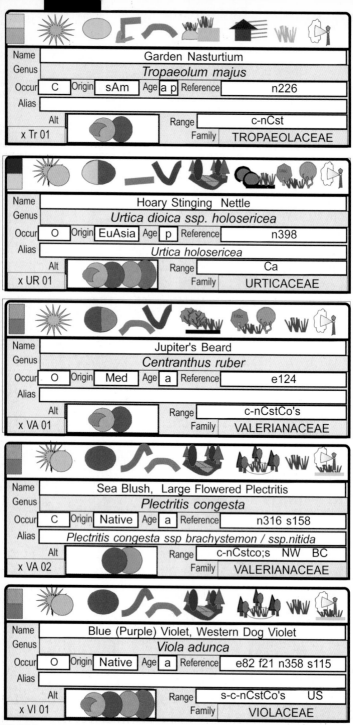

Garden Nasturtium

Name	Garden Nasturtium
Genus	*Tropaeolum majus*
Occur	C
Origin	sAm
Age	a p
Reference	n226
Alias	
Range	c-nCst
x Tr 01	
Family	TROPAEOLACEAE

Hoary Stinging Nettle

Name	Hoary Stinging Nettle
Genus	*Urtica dioica ssp. holosericea*
Occur	O
Origin	EuAsia
Age	p
Reference	n398
Alias	*Urtica holosericea*
Range	Ca
x UR 01	
Family	URTICACEAE

Jupiter's Beard

Name	Jupiter's Beard
Genus	*Centranthus ruber*
Occur	O
Origin	Med
Age	a
Reference	e124
Alias	
Range	c-nCstCo's
x VA 01	
Family	VALERIANACEAE

Sea Blush, Large Flowered Plectritis

Name	Sea Blush, Large Flowered Plectritis
Genus	*Plectritis congesta*
Occur	C
Origin	Native
Age	a
Reference	n316 s158
Alias	*Plectritis congesta ssp brachystemon / ssp.nitida*
Range	c-nCstco;s NW BC
x VA 02	
Family	VALERIANACEAE

Blue (Purple) Violet, Western Dog Violet

Name	Blue (Purple) Violet, Western Dog Violet
Genus	*Viola adunca*
Occur	O
Origin	Native
Age	a
Reference	e82 f21 n358 s115
Alias	
Range	s-c-nCstCo's US
x VI 01	
Family	VIOLACEAE

X 130

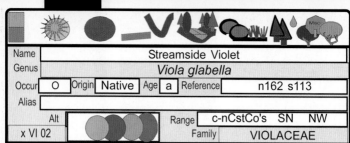

Name	Streamside Violet
Genus	*Viola glabella*
Occur	O	Origin	Native	Age	a	Reference	n162 s113
Alias	
Alt	Range	c-nCstCo's SN NW
x VI 02	Family	VIOLACEAE

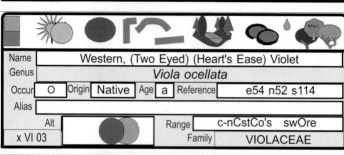

Name	Western, (Two Eyed) (Heart's Ease) Violet
Genus	*Viola ocellata*
Occur	O	Origin	Native	Age	a	Reference	e54 n52 s114
Alias	
Alt	Range	c-nCstCo's swOre
x VI 03	Family	VIOLACEAE

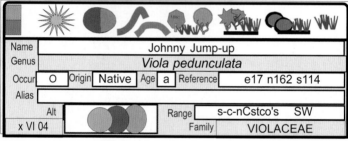

Name	Johnny Jump-up
Genus	*Viola pedunculata*
Occur	O	Origin	Native	Age	a	Reference	e17 n162 s114
Alias	
Alt	Range	s-c-nCstco's SW
x VI 04	Family	VIOLACEAE

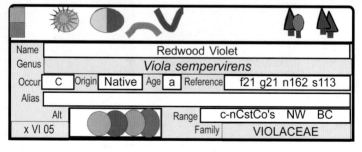

Name	Redwood Violet
Genus	*Viola sempervirens*
Occur	C	Origin	Native	Age	a	Reference	f21 g21 n162 s113
Alias	
Alt	Range	c-nCstCo's NW BC
x VI 05	Family	VIOLACEAE

X 134

X 135

Cupressus	
-- *goveniana* ssp. *goveniana*	G 2
-- *goveniana* ssp. *pigmaea*	G 2
-- *macrocarpa*	G 2
-- *pigmaea*	G 2
-- *sargentii*	G 2
Cuscuta *salina* var. *major*	X 116
Cynara *scolymus*	X 18
Cynodon *dactylon*	M 22
Cynoglossum *grande*	X 40
Cynosurus *echinatus*	M 22
Cyperus	
-- *eragrostis*	M 20
-- *strigosus*	M 20
-- *scoparius*	W 24
Dactylis *glomerata*	M 22
Delphinium	
-- *decorum* ssp. *decorum*	X 96
-- *hesperium* ssp. *hesperium*	X 96
-- *nudicaule*	X 98
-- *parryi* ssp. *biochmaniae*	X 98
-- *patens* ssp. *patens*	X 98
Dendromecon *rigida*	W 30
Dentaria *californica*	X 46
Dephinium	
-- *decorum*	X 96
-- *hesperium*	X 96
Deschampsia	
-- *caespitosa* ssp. *holciformis*	M 23
-- *holciformis*	M 23
Dianthys *velutinus*	X 50
Dicentra *formosa*	X 86
Dichelostemma	
-- *capitatum* ssp. *capitatum*	M 10
-- *congestum*	M 10
-- *multiflorum*	M 10
Dipsacus *sativus*	X 116
Disporum	
-- *hookeri*	M 10
-- *smithii*	M 12
Dodecatheon *hendersonii*	X 124
Dryopteris	
-- *arguta*	F 4
-- *austriaca*	F 4
-- *dilatata*	F 4
Duchesnea *indica*	X 100
Dudleya	
-- *cymosa* ssp *cymosa*	X 114
-- *farinosa*	X 114
-- *expansa*	F 4
Echium *candicans*	W 18
Echiveria	
-- *farinosa*	X 114
-- *laxa*	X 114

Elymus	
-- *californicus*	M 23
-- *multisetus*	M 23
Epilobium	
-- *watsonii*	
var. *francisanus*	X 84
var. *adenocaulon*	X 84
var. *occidentalis*	x 84
-- *californicum*	X 84
-- *canun* var. *canum*	X 84
-- *ciliatum* ssp. *ciliatum*	X 84
-- *ciliatum* ssp. *watsonii*	X 84
Equisetum	
-- *arvense*	F 2
-- *telmateia* var. *braunii*	F 2
Eremocarpus *setigerus*	X 116
Ericameria *arborescens*	W 16
-- *ericoides*	W 18
Erigeron *glaucus*	X 20
-- *karvinskianus*	X 20
Eriodictyon *californicum*	W 28
Eriogonum	
-- *latifolium*	X 90
-- *luteolum* var. *caninum*	X 90
-- *nudum*	X 90
-- *vimineum* v. *caninum*	X 90
Eriophyllum *confertiflorum*	
var. *confertiflorum*	X 20
-- *lanatum* v. *arachnoideum*	X 20
-- *staechadifolium*	
(incl var. *artemisiifolium*)	X 20
Erodium	
-- *botrys*	X 70
-- *cicutarium*	X 70
-- *moschatum*	X 72
Erysimum	
-- *concinnum*	X 46
-- *franciscanum*	X 46
-- *menziesii* ssp. *concinnum*	X 46
Eschscholzia *californica*	X 86
Eucalyptus *globulus*	W 12
Eupatorium *adenophora*	W 16
Festuca *californica*	M 23
Foeniculum *vulgare*	X 2
Fragaria *chiloensis*	X 100
-- *indica*	X 100
-- *vesca*	X 100
Franseria *chamissonis*	
ssp. *bipinnatisecta*	X 10
Fritillaria	
-- *affinis* var. *affinis*	M 12
-- *affinis* var. *tristulis*	M 12
-- *lanceolata*	M 12
-- *liliacea*	M 12
-- *lanceolata* v. *tristulis*	M 12

X 136

X 137

X 138

X 139

X 140

X 142

Gooseberry (Canyon)	W 28	Johnny Tuck (White)	X 110
Gooseberry (Menzies)	W 28	Juniper (Western)	G 2
Gooseberry (Straggly)	W 26	Jupiter's Beard	X 130
Grass (Bear) (Squaw)	M 18	Knotweed (Sand)	W 30
Grass (Bottlebrush (California))	M 23	Lacepod	X 48
Grass (Burmuda)	M 22	Larkspur (Coastal Prairie)	X 96
Grass (Dogtail)	M 22	Larkspur (Red) (Orange)	X 98
Grass (Hair, (Coastal Tufted))	M 23	Larkspur (Scrub)	X 98
Grass (Harding)	M 24	Larkspur (Western Coastal)	X 96
Grass (Little Rattlesnake)	M 22	Larkspur (Woodland Spreading)	X 98
Grass (Orchard)	M 22	Laural (California Bay)	W 10
Grass (Pampas)	M 22	Lettuce (Willow-leaf)	X 28
Grass (Rattlesnake)	M 22	Lily (Coastal)	M 14
Grass (Ripgut Brome)	M 22	Lily (Golden Globe)	M 6
Grass (Slim Oat)	M 22	Lily (Tiburon)	M 8
Grass (Velvet)	M 23	Lily (Yellow Mariposa)	M 6
Ground Cone		Lily (Yellow Star)	M 6
(California Brown)	X 120	Linanthus (Bristly)	X 88
Groundsel (Common)	X 34	Linanthus (Purplethroat)	X 88
Groundsel (Rayed)	X 34	Linanthus (Short Tubed)	X 88
Gumplant (Bay) (Marsh)	X 24	Linanthus (Small Flowered)	X 90
Gumplant (Marsh)	X 24	Lizardtail	X 20
Gumplant (Prostrate)	X 24	Long Rayed Hyacinth	M 16
Gumplant (San Francisco)	X 24	Lotus (California Subpinnate)	X 58
Gumplant (Seaside)	X 24	Lotus (Coastal)	X 56
Gumweed (Hairless-Hairy)	X 24	Lotus (Hairy Hill),	X 58
Hawkbit	X 30	Lotus (Small Flowered)	X 58
Hawkweed (White)	X 26	Lupine (Arroyo Blue)	X 60
Hazelnut (California)	W 18	Lupine (Coastal Bush)	W 24
Heather (Dune Mock)	W 18	Lupine (Coastal Prairie)	X 62
Heliotrope (Salt)	X 42	Lupine (False)	X 62
Hemlock (Poison)	X 2	Lupine (Giant bog)	X 60
Henbit (Red)	X 76	Lupine (Hollow Stem)	X 60
Honeysuckle (California)	X 114	Lupine (Miniature)	X 60
Honeysuckle (Twinberry)	W 4	Lupine (Secund)	X 60
Horkelia (California)	X 100	Lupine (Silverleaf)	W 24
Horsetail (Common)	F 2	Lupine (Sky)	X 60
Horsetail (Giant)	F 2	Lupine (Trailing)	X 62
Horseweed (Hairy)	X 18	Madia (Woodland)	X 30
Horseweed (Rayless)	X 18	Madrone (Pacific)	W 4
Hottentot Fig	W 14	Mahogany (Mountian)	W 12
Hounds tongue	X 40	Mallow (Checker)	X 80
Huckleberry (California Blue)	W 24	Mallow (Red)	X 80
Hyacinth (Wild)	M 10	Manroot (California)	X 116
Ice Plant (Pink)	W 14	Manroot (Coastal Oregon)	X 116
Indian warrior	X 108	Manzanita (Bolinas) (Marin)	W 22
Indians Dream	F 6	Manzanita (Fort Bragg)	W 22
Inside-out flower (Redwood)	X 112	Manzanita (Glandular Eastwood)	W 20
Iris (Coastal)	M 2	Manzanita (Mt. Tamalpais)	W 20
Iris (Douglas)	M 2	Manzanita (Pigmy Forest)	W 20
Iris (Ferdaldi's)	M 2	Maple (*Big leaf)	W 2
Iris (Ground)	M 4	Marram Grass	M 22
Jaumea	X 28	Melic Grass (California)	M 23
Jewelflower (Mt. Tamalpais)	X 48	Milk-maid (Woodland)	X 46
Jim Bush	W 34	Milkvetch (Brewer's)	X 54

Popcorn flower	X 42	Silver Beachbur	X 10
Poppy (Bush)	W 30	Silver Puffs	X 38
Poppy (California Golden)	X 86	Snakeroot (Pacific)	X 6
Pride of Madeira	W 18	Sneezeweed, Rosilla	X 24
Primrose (Beach Evening)	X 80	Snow Queen	X 108
Purple Musk Bush	W 32	Snowberry (Bush)	W 20
Pussy Ears	M 8	Soap Plant (Wavy Leaf)	M 8
Radish (Wild)	X 46	Solomon Seal (Fat) (Branched)	M 14
Ragwort (Purple)	X 34	Solomon Seal (Slim) (Star)	M 14
Ragwort (Tansy)	X 34	Sonoma Bentgrass	M 4
Rancher's fireweed	X 40	Sorrel (Redwood Wood)	X 122
Red Maids	X 92	Sorrel (Sheep)	X 92
Red Ribbons	X 82	Sour Grass	X 122
Red Ribbons (Santa Clara)	X 82	Sow-thistle (Prickly)	X 36
Redwood (Coastal)	G 6	Sow-thistle (Smooth Common)	X 36
Rhododendron (California)	W 22	Spikeweed (Common)	X 26
Rock Cress (Coastal) (Pink)	X 42	Spikewort (California)	X 112
Rock lettuce	X 114	Spring Gold	X 4
Rose (California Wild)	W 36	Spurrey (Corn)	X 52
Rose (Eglantine)	W 36	Spurry (Common Pink) (Sand)	X 52
Rose (Sweet Brier)	W 36	Squirreltail (Big)	M 23
Rose (Wood)	W 36	Star flower	X 126
Rush (Annual Roundheaded)	M 21	Star Tulip (Hairy)	M 8
Rush (Clustered)	M 21	Star Tulip (Marsh)	M 8
Rush (Inland)	M 21	Star Tulip (Oakland)	M 8
Rush (Long-fruited)	M 21	Starflower (Spring)	M 12
Rush (Western)	M 21	Starwort	X 52
Rush (Wood)	M 21	Stickwort	X 52
Rush Bolander's	M 21	Stonecrop (Spoon Leaved)	X 114
Rush Rose (Peak)	X 114	Strawberry (Beach)	X 100
Sage (Black)	W 30	Strawberry (Mock)	X 100
Sage (Pitcher)	W 28	Strawberry (Wild Wood))	X 100
Sagebrush (California)	X 12	Sun Cup	X 82
Sagewort (Beach)	X 12	Sunflower	X 26
Sailer Caps	X 124	Sunflower (Seaside Woolly)	X 20
Salal	w 22	Sunflower (Woolly)	X 20
Salmonberry	W 38	Sweet Alyssum	X 46
Salsify	X 38	Sycamore (Western)	W 12
Sandwort (Perennial)	X 50	Tackstem	X 12
Sandwort (Serpentine)	X 50	Tanoak	W 6
Sanicle (Lace Leaf) (Coast)	X 6	Tarplant (Fragrant Coastal)	X 26
Sanicle (RedPurple)	X 6	Tarplant (Spiny)	X 26
Sea Blush	X 130	Tarweed (Slender)	X 30
Sea Fig	W 14	Tarweed (Tall Coast)	X 32
Sea Lettuce	X 114	Teasel (White) (Fuller's)	X 116
Sea Pink	X 124	Thimbleberry	W 36
Sea Rocket	X 44	Thistle (Barnaby's)	X 14
Sedge	M 20	Thistle (Blue Star)	X 38
Sedge (Round Fruited)	M 20	Thistle (Brownie)	X 18
Sedge (Umbrella)	M 20	Thistle (Bull)	X 18
Selfheal (Large Flower)	X 78	Thistle (Cobwebby)	X 16
Shepard's purse	X 44	Thistle (Indian)	X 16
Sheperd's Needle	X 8	Thistle (Italian)	X 14
Shooting Star, Mosquito Bills,	X 124	Thistle (Milk)	X 36
Silk Tassel Bush (Lowland)	W 10	Thistle (Mt Tamalpais)	X 16

X 146

X 147